Stop Drinking and Start Living
Second Edition

Stop Drinking and Start Living
Second Edition

Stephen E. Schlesinger, Ph.D.
& John J. Gillick, Ph.D.

 Human Services Institute

TAB BOOKS Inc.
Blue Ridge Summit, PA

Antabuse is Ayerst Laboratories' registered trademark for the drug disulfiram.

SECOND EDITION
FIRST PRINTING

Library of Congress Cataloging in Publication Data

Schlesinger, Stephen E.
    Stop drinking and start living.

    Includes index.
    1. Alcoholics—Rehabilitation—United States.
2. Alcoholism—United States. 3. Alcoholism—Treatment—
United States. I. Gillick, John J. II. Title.
HV5279.S35 1989   362.2′92   88-35646
ISBN 0-8306-3227-1 (pbk.)

TAB BOOKS Inc. offers software for sale. For information and a catalog, please contact TAB Software Department, Blue Ridge Summit, PA 17294-0850.

Questions regarding the content of this book should be addressed to:

Reader Inquiry Branch
TAB BOOKS Inc.
Blue Ridge Summit, PA 17294-0214

Acquisitions Editor: Kim Tabor
Manuscript Editor: Steven H. Mesner

Cover photograph by Susan Riley, Harrisonburg, Virginia.

Contents

Preface

This book is written for those who have drinking problems and for those who know someone who drinks too much. It focuses on a problem of ever-increasing national visibility, and it grew out of our clinical work. In our treatment of drinkers and their families we have discovered that many people are not familiar with basic information about alcohol and that they do not understand their own behavior. By the time they come to us, their drinking has usually reached rather destructive proportions. Had they understood more sooner, they might have sought help earlier.

We know from our clinical work and from the work of our colleagues that more people are coming for treatment of drinking problems now than previously. Perhaps this is because of the recent exposure by many well-known Americans of their problems with alcohol. The wife of one President and the brother of another, several United States Congressmen and members of their families, and many show business personalities and athletes have publicly revealed the courses of their drinking careers and their attempts to combat the problems that their drinking caused.

But we also know that there are many drinkers and their families who have not yet decided whether they need help to tackle their drinking problems.

So, then, is this book for everyone? No, it is not; it is

for *you*, if you have any connection with a drinking problem—yours or someone else's.

In writing this volume we have had *you* in mind, and we have given you the information and tools to wage your battle with a drinking problem. Even so, in such an effort, you still may need help. To that end we have included a list of resources available to offer you that extra assistance. We are hopeful that, with this book and those resources, yours will be a successful campaign when you tackle it.

As you read this book, you will notice that we have referred to drinkers in the masculine gender, as "he" and "him." This is not to draw your attention only to male drinkers or to suggest that our approach to alcoholism is male-oriented. Neither is the case; our approach is as unbiased as the drinking problems we treat. Alcoholism is as much a problem for women as it is for men. By electing to refer only to one gender in our writing, we have attempted to make reading the book somewhat less complicated. Reading a lot of "he/shes" and "him/hers," we guessed, would be as distracting for you as it is for us.

Lastly, a project like this is nurtured by the inspiration and support of a number of people whose contributions may not be evident from the finished product. The idea for this book developed over time as a result of the need for information our patients have had when they have come to us for treatment. The book itself took shape with the understanding and patience of our wives, Marilyn and Susan, and our children, Nora, Aaron, Kate, and Anne as we wrote several preliminary drafts. Dr. Ina Schlesinger's repeated readings of our manuscripts helped us mold the book into its final form. Her comments on organization, clarity, and style provided a much-needed and greatly appreciated viewpoint on our work which kept us on course. And Kathie Webb's patience as she typed drafts of our chapters was an invaluable aid to the preparation of the final manuscript.

So the thoughts in this book may be ours, but the influence of our families and friends can be felt in their expression here.

Introduction to the Second Edition

In the several years since *Stop Drinking and Start Living* was published, there have been many developments both in the identification and treatment of addictions and in our own approach to these problems. We have noted with interest the broadening of the definitions of addictive problems and the growing awareness of common components among them, regardless of the particular substance used (e.g., alcohol, other drugs, food) or the behaviors involved (e.g., gambling, excessive spending). Addictions may present themselves differently, but the underlying mechanisms that sustain them may share a good deal more in common than many people originally believed.

We have been heartened by the growing awareness that the pain suffered by relatives and close friends of excessive drinkers and other addicts is both acute and treatable. In the ensuing years, the residual effects of addictions in families have been recognized in the children who grew up unshielded from their destructive impacts.

All of these developments have moved forward our understanding of the complexities of addictions, and they have pointed the way to the improvements and additions we have made in this revised edition of *Stop Drinking and Start Living*.

With this background, we present this second edition

of *Stop Drinking and Start Living*. Our hope is that we are able to reach out more effectively to drinkers and to those of their family members and friends who are concerned about them and about the effects of their drinking on those whose lives they touch. We offer a renewed hope that drinking problems can be understood and overcome and that no one—drinkers or those affected by their drinking—need endure the pain the problems cause. We trust that your journey to health will be fruitful and rewarding, and we are pleased to join you in that effort.

Introduction

Drinking is as American as apple pie. For millions of Americans, however, drinking has gotten out of hand. Alcohol abuse is one of this nation's major health problems.

This book can help you understand alcohol and its abuse. It can help you if you think you may have a problem with your own drinking. It can also be helpful to you if someone close to you has a drinking problem.

There are several major points to consider. Let us briefly outline the first three of them here. We will get to the others later.

☐ Alcohol problems don't have to be feared.
☐ Alcohol problems can be understood as easily as other problems.
☐ People with alcohol problems can be helped.

Alcohol Problems Don't Have to Be Feared. Problem drinkers and their families are often frightened by what they see as a perplexing problem. Alcohol abuse is shrouded in an aura of mystery that frequently carries with it a subtle moral dilemma and a definite social stigma. Some people think drinking is the "manly" or social thing to do. They condone getting drunk, or consider it funny. Others, though, condemn it as a moral outrage.

In addition, those with drinking problems often feel caught between a rock and a hard place. Even though drinking may be doing them some harm, it may be frightening to think about actually giving it up. "What will happen? Can I pull it off?"

But people do not have to be afraid of drinking problems or of giving up drinking. The problems must be recognized as such, but no one need surrender to their seeming inevitability. Alcohol problems are not hopeless, and problem drinkers and their families need not feel helpless to deal with them.

Alcohol Problems Can Be Understood as Other Problems Can. Sometimes it is difficult to step back and take a look at our problems—and so it is with alcohol problems. But, like other problems, alcohol problems *can* be understood. It might be hard not to think of a drinking problem as hopeless. It is often all too easy to believe you are helpless to do anything about it. Though it may seem sometimes that each stage a drinker passes through is an unavoidable consequence of the one preceding it, alcohol problems need not necessarily go continually downhill. Hope will come from taking a hard and honest look at the problem. You *can* understand a drinking problem and it *can* be treated, even if your drinking now seems to be an uncontrollable force against you.

People with Alcohol Problems Can Be Helped. Successful treatment begins with understanding. Understanding alcohol problems in turn means recognizing that they are often related to other problems in people's lives. Drinking often serves a purpose. Problem drinkers usually *get* something from drinking even though they may not immediately understand what that is. People often believe it helps them deal with life's difficulties. But they always *give up* something, too. Drinking becomes a problem when the things people give up begin to bother them. This is the point at which treatment may be necessary.

For some, drinking may come to affect job performance, and they may have to give up a job or be fired. For others, it may be that family life begins to suffer. In general, the problems that drinking causes are quite evident. Problem drinkers usually know what alcohol is forcing them to "give up." What may be less clear is what people "get" from drinking. This is a common focus of treatment. If drinkers can learn other ways to "get" what they need, it may become less necessary for them to use alcohol.

A Word about a Word

You will notice that we haven't used the word *alcoholic* so far. In fact, we won't use it at all in this book when we talk about drinkers. We won't use it because for some people it has a very negative ring to it. A stigma seems to be attached to the term. Many connect it with "bad" or "immoral" people. We want to avoid reinforcing these connections. People who have problems with their drinking certainly share two things—they drink too much, and it is causing problems for them. This describes problem drinkers by their behavior, by what they do. It makes no judgments about them as people.

It also assumes that not all drinkers are the same. Saying that all problem drinkers are alike simply because they all drink excessively is like saying all people who have chest pains are necessarily victims of heart disease. Only certain types of symptoms indicate heart disease, and not all cardiac patients have chest pains. By the same token, different drinking patterns suggest different types of drinking problems, so here we will not worry about giving the drinking a label. Instead, we will try to learn all we can about drinking problems and try to find out what treatment is all about.

The Numbers

Two-thirds of the adults and a like proportion of adolescents in this country drink with some regularity. We Americans drink lots of alcohol. In 1982, for instance, we drank 5.56 *billion* gallons of beer. One industry prediction forecasts that during the remainder of the decade, beer consumption will rise by 20 percent, wine consumption by

115 percent, and the consumption of liquor somewhere between those two figures.

Clearly, not all who drink do so excessively, but those who do have a substantial impact on our society. The problems caused by excessive drinking—usually called *alcoholism*—are enormous. It is estimated that they include as many as 12,000,000 adults and 3,500,000 adolescents and children in the United States. Government studies conclude that 14 percent of Americans will develop alcohol abuse problems at some time in their lives.

Beyond drinkers themselves, it has been estimated that, on average, each drinker significantly affects the lives of four others close to him (parents, a spouse, children, friends). When you include these people, the total number of people affected by drinking problems may exceed 50 million.

Excessive drinking may cost American business between 40 and 45 *billion* dollars each year in lost work time, lower productivity, and injuries. The United States Department of Transportation has estimated that drinking drivers and intoxicated pedestrians contribute each year to 25,000 traffic deaths and at least 800,000 vehicle accidents. It has been demonstrated that the average drinking driver can increase by *100 times* the chances that he will be responsible for a car crash. The Secretary of Defense recently reported that in our peacetime armed forces, drunken driving "is the leading cause of death." Indeed, 14 percent of American military personnel can be classified as heavy drinkers.

Alcohol use can be associated with up to 50 percent of all arrests (one million arrests annually for public intoxication alone, costing the justice system an estimated $300 million) and perhaps 40 percent of the cases brought before the nation's family courts each year. Alcohol can account for 15 percent of the nation's health care costs, and it may contribute to one-third of the suicides and two-thirds of the homicides recorded each year. One in five television reporters and anchors on evening news programs regularly drink heavily enough—or use enough other drugs—to interfere with their work. And the list goes on and on. It comes as no surprise, then, that the Consumer Federation of America listed alcohol as the third most dangerous consumer product on the market today.

Add it all up, according to a United States Senate subcommittee, and alcoholism's annual price tag may exceed $100 billion—*a hundred billion* dollars, not counting the human suffering.

When you take into account the number of people with drinking problems, those they affect, and the consequences all those problem drinkers have on our economy, alcoholism certainly qualifies as one of the most pressing health problems our country faces. Indeed, polls show that we know that. Already 80 percent of us see alcohol abuse as a major national problem, and it was the second priority listed in the report of the recent White House Conference on Families.

It may come as something of a surprise, then, to learn that only about 15 percent of alcohol abusers actually end up getting treatment for the alcohol problems that may shorten their life expectancies by as much as 10 to 12 years. Under some conditions, such as drinking and driving, life expectancy can be shortened even more.

Alcohol-related Traffic Accidents

A great deal of debate has been generated lately about the role alcohol plays in traffic accidents. When the President's Task Force on Drunk Driving released its report recently, the issue was thrust even more forcefully into the spotlight of national attention, and the debate heated up considerably.

This is not an idle debate. Alcohol plays a major role in traffic-related injuries, death, and property damage. While most estimates suggest that alcohol may play a role in half of our traffic deaths each year, results of a series of studies reported recently by the College of American Pathologists suggested that the figure may be much higher—perhaps as high as 90 percent.

Overall, highway crashes follow heart disease, cancer, and stroke as the leading cause of death among Americans. For those under 40, they are the *leading* cause of death. Drunk driving is probably the largest single *preventable* cause of accidents.

Typically, a driver is said to be *intoxicated* legally if the concentration of alcohol in his blood is 0.10 percent or greater. Almost universally, if a driver is arrested for suspicion of driving under the influence of alcohol (referred to as DUI) and if the alcohol in his blood exceeds this concentration, he is considered to be intoxicated. If his blood alcohol level is less than 0.10 but equal to or greater than 0.05, he is said to be *impaired*. According to the laws in most states, people with concentrations of alcohol in their blood between 0.01 and 0.05 are neither legally intoxicated nor legally impaired. However, because alcohol can affect people's functioning even at low levels, alcohol may be *involved* in traffic accidents even if the amount of alcohol in a person's blood is below the legal limit. The chart on page xvii describes the increasing effects alcohol has on our actions as the level of alcohol in the blood increases.

The statistics on alcohol-related traffic accidents are frightening, and they apply both to drivers and to pedestrians.

Driver Fatalities

More than half the drivers killed each year in car crashes on our highways are legally intoxicated at the time of their fatal accidents. This number applies equally to drivers of cars and motorcycles. If impaired drivers are included in these statistics, the numbers jump another five percent or so. Including those whose driving judgment has been affected at all by alcohol (whether the alcohol in their blood exceeds the limits specified by the law), it is estimated that perhaps 60 percent of fatal car crashes involve alcohol. As you can see in the chart on the next page, the chances of causing a fatal accident increase as the amount of alcohol in the driver's blood increases.

Blood alcohol concentration and probability of fatal accident.

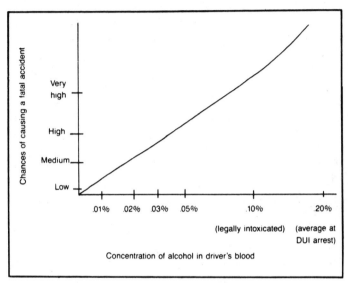

Pedestrian Fatalities

One of every five traffic fatalities is a pedestrian, and almost all are 14 years of age or older. Of the pedestrians killed each year in traffic accidents, half have been drinking. Most of these are either intoxicated or impaired by the amount of alcohol in their blood.

Other Accidents

Alcohol clearly plays a role in accidents in which some-one—a driver, a passenger, or a pedestrian—is killed. But alcohol also plays a role in accidents that injure but do not kill, and in accidents that cause damage only to property. Current estimates are that alcohol is involved in up to one-quarter of traffic-related injuries and in approximately eight percent of the property damage done by vehicle crashes.

There are several things which seem to be related to alcohol-related accidents. First, about three-quarters of alcohol-related traffic deaths occur at night, or at dawn or dusk, when light conditions are poor. Second, younger drivers tend to present a greater risk of involvement in an alcohol-related crash than do older drivers, as you can see in the chart on page xix. In terms of absolute numbers of alcohol-related accidents, male drivers between the ages of 21 and 35 present the greatest risk of any group.

Arrests for DUI

Each year over one million adults are arrested for DUI. As high as this number seems, though, these are only the drivers who attract the attention of the police. It is estimated that for each arrest, perhaps a thousand DUI incidents go unnoticed.

On average, DUI offenders have a concentration of alcohol in their blood of 0.20, or twice the legal level of intoxication. As you can see from the chart on page xvii, a person with that much alcohol in his blood will likely be quite disabled. Yet some people claim they can learn to overcome these alcohol-induced disabilities and drive regularly—and safely!—even after drinking heavily. Usually, however, this conclusion is the result of poor powers of observation brought on by the heavy drinking itself—the person is simply too impaired to notice his own actions.

What is clear is that the effects of alcohol do not discriminate—they affect our actions no matter what we are doing. If we are at home, our intoxication likely is harmless, so long as we are not violently drunk. If we are behind the wheel of a ton and a half of steel, though, it can be deadly—both for us and for those with or around us. *That* is what all the fuss is about.

Alcohol problems know no boundaries of age, sex, race, education, profession, or ethnic background. They affect many different types of people. There is really no such thing as an "average" problem drinker. Popular conceptions notwithstanding, less than five percent of all problem drinkers might fit the "skid row bum" description. So the

Relative contribution of drivers' ages to alcohol-involved accidents.

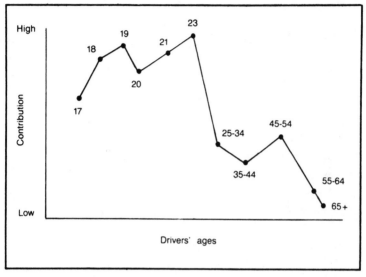

fact that someone is not a "skid row bum" does not mean, by itself, that he or she doesn't have an alcohol problem.

The important thing to derive from all the numbers is that many different types of people have problems with their drinking and that drinking problems come in all shapes and sizes.

Clearly, the more people understand about this problem and the sooner they act, the better able they will be to help themselves or those close to them. People do not have to hit "rock bottom" before they can be helped. And there are things that can be done about the problems caused by drinking even before the drinker has decided to stop drinking.

The thrust of this book, then, is this: People have different ways of coping with the difficulties that confront each of us. Some of those ways are effective and others are not. In this latter category are smoking too much, eating too much, or stressing the body in other ways to produce a host of physical symptoms. Ulcers and some types of headaches fall into this category. And some people drink too much.

The process of reversing this problem begins with an understanding of the effect alcohol has on the body and proceeds to an understanding of why a person continues to drink in the face of obvious physical and psychological damage. It ends by finding ways to cope with difficulties other than drinking.

How Do You Tell If Someone Has a Problem with Alcohol?

There is no single way to judge whether a person's drinking is problematic. It is often a judgment that is made after carefully assessing the person's drinking (how much and when), its effect on him physically and emotionally, and its effect on those around him—primarily family members, friends, employers, and the law.

We mentioned earlier that there is no "average" drinker. There is also no single set of criteria which defines the problem drinker. Some drinkers seem "typically" problematic while others may not. Consider these two cases:

For the better part of 25 years, Marvin has been drunk at least four times a week. His wife has lost count of the jobs he has lost as a result of poor attendance and even poorer performance. He has been in the hospital 18 times for major, alcohol-related problems. Twice he has almost died in the intensive care unit of complications following extremely heavy—even for Marvin—drinking episodes. He has been arrested six times for drunken driving and has lost his license. He registered for another license under a friend's name and lost that one, too. His "rap sheet" in the police computer is 17 pages long and includes over 75 arrests for driving under the influence of alcohol and for being drunk and disorderly. *Everyone* thinks Marvin's drinking is a problem—except Marvin.

Ted's problem, however, is not quite so obvious. Unlike Marvin, Ted has not been arrested for drunk driving or for being drunk and disorderly. Had he been, he might have lost his license to practice law. And that would have ruined what most people agree is a brilliant career.

Ted is a first-class criminal attorney. He has represented both the famous and the infamous in his hometown and across the country. He has been pleased over the years by what he calls his "name recognition in the media." He is not the most famous attorney in the country, but it is not for lack of effort. Ted would say that it is only that he is not *yet* the best known.

But Ted drinks, and he drinks a lot. If you ask him, he'll tell you his drinking fits his profession. "That's how my business goes," he'll tell you. And he'll tell you he can handle it. If you ask those around him, they'll tell you he functions very well.

But not that well. Ask his secretary, and she'll tell you about a different Ted—about the incomplete briefs he writes, about the lapses of memory, about the growing number of times Ted is sick these days and about the bottles of vodka he stocks in the office so he'll always have one for his briefcase. Ask his former wife and his kids, and they'll tell you about his drunken stupors when he would tear up the house and then disappear from home and office for a week. And ask Ted's doctor—in fact, any of the *five* he's shuttled among in the past two years as he searched for encouraging news about his liver and pancreas—and he'll tell you about all the things that may not be visible to us. Ted doesn't fit our stereotype of a problem drinker—not until we look more closely, that is.

All this may seem pretty indefinite, but there are some ways to find out whether or not someone has a drinking problem. First, you can ask whether the drinking has affected the person's physical and emotional well-being. Has alcohol caused the person to become ill? Have his moods or behavior changed while drinking? Have you noticed (or have other people commented) that he seems to have become different over a period of time for no apparent reason besides the drinking? Has someone suggested he get help for his drinking?

Second, you can ask whether his relationships have

been affected. Has drinking caused problems in his family? With his friends?

Third, you can ask whether the person's job has been affected. Has he missed work because of his drinking? Has he been reprimanded by his employer or warned that his job may be on the line because of poor performance or too many missed days? Has he been referred to an "employee assistance program," an employer-sponsored program to help employees who have problems, including with drinking?

Fourth, you can ask whether the person has had trouble with the law because of drinking. Has he been arrested for being drunk and disorderly? Has he been charged with driving under the influence of alcohol (so-called "drunk driving")?

In general, the more areas in which alcohol has had a bad effect, the more likely it is that a person's drinking is problematic, even if the effects are not immediately visible and even if the person denies the problems.

If there *is* such a problem, knowledge about the serious physical damage alcohol can do to the body may be the first item that needs discussion.

PART 1
What Alcohol Does

Chapter 1

Alcohol and the Body

There are many substances that are *toxic*—that is, poisonous—to the human body. The body cannot handle some of these substances, and as a result we may get seriously ill or even die when they enter our bodies. But there are some toxic substances the body *can* handle. Alcohol is one of these.

Alcohol is toxic to the body, but the body has a way to get rid of it. This process is call *metabolizing* alcohol, and the major part of this job is handled by the liver. The liver metabolizes 90 to 95 percent of the alcohol that enters the body. Between 5 and 10 percent leaves the body, unchanged, in exhaled air, urine, and perspiration.

The body is set up to get rid of certain toxins—including alcohol—primarily because those toxins are common byproducts of various bodily functions. Each day, in the process of digesting our food, tiny organisms in the intestine convert sugar to alcohol. The alcohol enters the bloodstream and is metabolized as soon as it reaches the liver.

We produce only a small amount of alcohol naturally in our bodies and we produce it at a relatively slow rate. The average healthy liver can meet this demand and can metabolize about three-quarters to one ounce of 90-proof spirits or about 8 to 12 ounces of beer each hour. That's about one drink or one beer per hour.

When we feel the effects of our drinking, it is because drinking alcohol easily overloads the liver's ability to metabolize it. As this overload occurs, some of the alcohol we take in stays in the bloodstream until the liver can catch up and metabolize it.

When it is in the bloodstream, alcohol circulates through the body and begins to interfere with the ways different parts of the body function. If we allow alcohol to circulate long enough and often enough, it can begin to kill body cells—and, eventually, the organs those cells make up.

ALCOHOL AS FOOD

Alcohol is, among other things, a food. Like other foods, it contains calories. But unlike other foods, it does not have to be digested. It is absorbed into the body as is. And alcohol is useless nutritionally. It offers little, if any, sustenance. The calories it contains are *empty calories*.

The caloric content of alcohol is quite high. Calculating the caloric content of drinks is pretty straightforward. In scientific terms, one gram of pure alcohol produces about seven calories. But no drink is *pure* alcohol, and not all beverages have the same amount of alcohol in them. In practical terms, we get about 100 calories by drinking any one of the following: 12 ounces of beer, 1.5 ounces of rum, 1.5 ounces of whiskey, 2 ounces of port wine, or about 3 ounces of sherry. By comparison, there are 100 calories in 2 tablespoons of sugar. Even if we drink relatively moderately, alcohol can account for a sizable portion of our daily caloric needs. Unlike other foods, however, alcohol can also have a rapid physical effect on us.

HOW DRUNK, HOW FAST?

The two most important factors that affect the amount of alcohol entering the body are the type of beverage a person drinks and the speed at which he drinks it. The rate at which the body absorbs alcohol may vary slightly according to several factors, and these may affect the time it takes people to feel that first "glow" after they start drinking. Mixers can affect the rate of absorption. Mixing a drink with plain water seems to reduce the rate of absorption slightly. Mixing it with carbonated water, however, tends to speed up absorption—you will feel the effects of a scotch and soda before those of a scotch and water.

A second influence on absorption comes from psychological factors. Stress or nervousness can increase the speed at which the stomach empties its contents into the intestines, where most alcohol is absorbed. In general, the more nervous a person is, the shorter time it takes the stomach to empty and the more quickly the alcohol will be absorbed into the blood.

Third, the rate at which the body absorbs alcohol is greater when the stomach is empty than when it contains food. And fourth, the amount of muscle tissue a person has seems to affect the level of alcohol in the blood. The more muscle, the less concentrated the alcohol tends to be when it reaches the brain.

The important things we know so far, then, are these: The liver is the only organ that can metabolize alcohol in the body. When a person puts alcohol in his body faster than the liver can handle it, an excess of alcohol builds up in the blood until the liver can eliminate it. We cannot speed up the rate at which the liver metabolizes alcohol. Nothing, in other words, can speed up the sobering-up process—not black coffee, not cold showers—nothing.

With these things in mind, let us turn our attention now to the manner in which alcohol affects our health when we drink excessively.

ALCOHOL AND HEALTH

Alcohol wears many hats. We've seen that it is a food. Now we'll look at it as a drug—a drug that can affect a person's health in a number of ways. In the *short* run, excessive drinking is frequently the indirect cause of health problems, though in a healthy person, occasional excessive drinking may not do permanent damage to the body. But even occasional excessive drinking can reduce a person's judgment, his ability to react quickly to dangerous situations, and his ability to make good decisions. Interfering with these abilities makes people more vulnerable to accident and injury. We know, for instance, that people who drink and drive can increase their chances of being involved in accidents by as much as 100 times. And we know that drinking can increase the risk of on-the-job accidents by as much as three times.

In the *longer* run, however, alcohol can damage a drinker's physical and emotional health directly. As a person drinks more and more heavily, the body attempts to adjust to the increased amounts of alcohol it has to handle. A person may notice as time passes that it takes more and more alcohol to get the same feeling he got from drinking in the past. This phenomenon is called *tolerance*. Briefly, what happens is that the central nervous system—the switchboard of the body, which regulates bodily functions —adjusts as much as it can to the increased amounts of alcohol. It is not, as some believe, a demonstration of prowess. So if you know someone who can "really put it away," he doesn't possess some unusual skill or remarkable strength. His large capacity is due to his body's adjustment to a poison—and it is a *warning sign* that his drinking may be out of hand.

These are some of the ways that the body tries to adjust to the increased alcohol that floods it, but they are actually emergency measures, and like all emergency measures, they cannot be used forever. In the long run, if the alcohol intake does not decrease, the body's resources are simply overwhelmed. Quite soon, the excess circulating alcohol begins to affect almost all areas and all functions of the body.

Alcohol and Sleep

Heavy doses of alcohol are known to interfere with a particularly important phase of sleep known as Rapid Eye Movement, or REM, sleep. If a person is deprived of adequate REM sleep, as he might be when drinking heavily, it is likely that he will appear irritable, tired, and nervous. Further, he may have trouble remembering things accurately or paying full attention to what he is doing.

Sleep patterns usually return to normal when drinking is halted, but the time they take to return to normal is directly related to the amount of alcohol a person was drinking. The more and the longer the person drank, the longer it takes for sleep to return to normal.

Alcohol and Sex

Shakespeare hit the nail on the head when he said that alcohol "provides the desire, but taketh away the performance." In the short run, alcohol can reduce inhibitions and increase sexual desire as it begins to have its effect on the brain. But it also interferes with sexual functioning. Among other things, it can be difficult for men to achieve and maintain satisfactory erections, and it may be difficult for both men and women to concentrate enough on the sexual experience to make it a satisfying one.

Prolonged heavy drinking, though, can have much more serious effects on the lives of drinkers. First, it is often the case that the sex lives of heavy drinkers are disrupted. They have sexual relations less often, and the quality of their experiences declines markedly. But, second, heavy drinking can contribute to early degeneration of male sexual organs, a permanent change with important effects on the drinker's desire for sex and ability to perform sexually. This effect is related to alcohol's effect on the production and breakdown of the male hormone testosterone. The effects on sexual feelings and performance can have a psychological impact on the drinker's marital and other initimate relationships.

Alcohol and the Central Nervous System

The noticeable first effects of an excess of alcohol circulating in the body are difficulties with the central nervous system—the brain and nerves. The higher the concentration of alcohol in the blood, the more profound the effects on the central nervous system.

The concentration of alcohol in the bloodstream is called the Blood Alcohol Concentration (BAC), and it is expressed as the amount of alcohol per volume of blood.

A typical drink has about .75 ounce of alcohol in it. You can get this by drinking a shot of spirits (1.5 ounce of 80 to 100-proof liquor), a 12-ounce can of beer (5 to 6 percent alcohol) or a glass of wine (5 ounces of wine with 12 to 15 percent alcohol). One drink will raise the BAC of an average 150-pound person to .02 percent and will be metabolized by a healthy liver in about an hour. At this BAC, most people begin to feel a little differently. But at the drinking rate of one drink each hour, little alcohol accumulates in the blood, and the feeling usually passes quickly.

As you can see from the table on the next page, however, the effects escalate rather dramatically if that person drinks more than one drink per hour.

At first glance, you might wonder how anyone could reach a BAC of .43 or above. Two examples are "chugging contests" and college fraternity initiation rites, in which people drink as much as they can as quickly as they can. These can lead to very high BACs. But it is worth remembering that before giving up entirely, the body can develop a tolerance for a *huge* amount of alcohol. It is not unusual for some drinkers to drink a quart of liquor or case of beer —or more—each day. The largest verified consumption encountered by the authors was that of a large patient who drank three quarts of whiskey *each day* after work.

As a result of large intakes of alcohol over a period of time, the body may tolerate a BAC that might prove fatal to the average drinker. For example, the blood alcohol test of another person we treated showed a BAC of .51—substantially above the level at which we might have expected him to die. Yet he walked into the hospital and, while the blood test was being analyzed, calmly talked to other patients while he ate his lunch. His body had learned to tolerate enormous amounts of alcohol. Obviously, he is a rare exception to the general rule. Either a person's reactions

Effects of Alcohol.

Average Number of Drinks per hour	BAC	Effects
1	.02%	Flushing of skin; heart speeds up a bit.
2	.04%	Feeling of relaxation begins.
3	.06%	Judgment is slower; coordination is more difficult; giddiness sets in.
4	.08%	Coordination deteriorates further; perception is altered.
5	.10%	Legally intoxicated in most states; vision getting blurred; reaction time slows down; speech getting slurred; poor control of muscles.
8	.16%	Staggering, double vision; loss of balance.
16	.32%	Person may lose consciousness or not react to those around him.
20	.40%	Person loses consciousness and is not easily aroused; pupils are dilated; skin is cool and moist.
over 20	.43% +	Person usually dies of respiratory arrest.

roughly follow the effects outlined in the table above, or he has become tolerant to alcohol and has a problem with his drinking.

Alcohol causes the increasingly detrimental effects listed in the table by interfering with the way in which brain cells work. It begins by interfering with the way electricity is transmitted both inside of and between brain cells. As a result, the message cells send to one another become distorted and we find it harder to control ourselves than we do when we are sober.

Next, alcohol is an anesthetic to the central nervous system. It slows down the functioning of nerve cells. It also appears that alcohol interferes with the manner in which brain cells use oxygen. So brain cells end up functioning in both a disorganized *and* a slower fashion.

Eventually, long-term drinking can kill enough brain cells to alter the structure of the brain itself and even cause it to shrink in size. These effects on the brain are permanent and can disable the drinker's ability to reason, remember, and think.

In some cases, prolonged heavy drinking leads to decreased feeling in various parts of the body, particularly in the hands and feet, legs and arms. This condition, called *peripheral neuropathy*, is usually the result of a drinker's drinking, although it can result from other factors. If it is caught early on, it is likely that the nerve damage can be reversed, if drinking ceases. If not, it may progress.

In the worst of cases, long-term drinking destroys important functions of the brain. Perhaps you've heard of a "wet brain" syndrome, named the Wernicke-Korsakoff syndrome after the doctors who first described it. It begins with difficulties seeing, feeling, and balancing while walking. The person is out of touch with people and things around him. He cannot tell you where he is or what day or year it is. He also does not respond to those around him and cannot carry on a conversation. At this point (the Wernicke stage), some medical treatments may clear up the condition. Doses of the B vitamins seem particularly helpful.

But if drinking continues, the condition can become much worse—even permanently so. The Korsakoff stage involves profound changes in the drinker's personality and mental abilities. He cannot remember old things, and he cannot learn new things without a major effort by those caring for him. Korsakoff patients frequently invent elaborate and ridiculous stories to compensate for their memory problems. They become physically weak, emotionally withdrawn, and largely oblivious to their surroundings. They cannot take care of themselves and must be cared for constantly for the rest of their lives. It is a cruel irony that the Korsakoff patient usually no longer has the wherewithal to drink. But it is too late: the alcohol has long since done its damage.

The Wernicke-Korsakoff syndrome represents damage to the brain at the end of a career of persistant abusive drinking. Alcohol can have effects on other parts of the body as well, and we will now briefly follow alcohol on its destructive journey through those parts of the body.

Alcohol and the Mouth and Throat

Alcohol's travels begin in the mouth and throat. Indeed, about 20 percent of the alcohol we drink is absorbed into the body directly from the mouth and throat.

Compared to its effects on other parts of the body, alcohol's effect on the mouth and throat is usually less frequently seen. However, research evidence suggests that heavy drinking over a long period greatly increases the drinker's chances of developing cancer of the mouth and throat. Further, it appears that this cancer risk is increased substantially if the heavy drinker is also a heavy smoker.

Alcohol and the Esophagus

The esophagus is the tube that connects the mouth and throat with the stomach. Prolonged heavy drinking has been associated with irritation and bleeding of the esophagus. These can merely be uncomfortable for the drinker, and they may respond to medical treatment, but they may also become life-threatening if they get worse with more drinking.

Another medical consequence usually *is* life-threatening. This is cancer of the esophagus. Research suggests that heavy drinking may contribute more to this type of cancer than does smoking.

Alcohol and the Stomach

The next stop for alcohol is the stomach. When it arrives, it slows down the process by which the stomach empties its contents into the intestines. At the same time, alcohol increases the production of acid in the stomach. One result: Stomach problems are frequently found among heavy drinkers. The most common of these are gastritis, an inflammation of the stomach walls, and ulcers, which are raw sores in the stomach wall.

Over time, rather than leading to excess stomach acid, alcohol seems to reduce the stomach's ability to produce the acid it needs for proper digestion.

Though these usually are not immediate threats to the drinker's life, they can be very serious for some. When people begin to bleed heavily from the stomach and nearby areas, they need immediate medical attention. Without treatment, the bleeding can become life-threatening.

Alcohol and the Intestines

The job of the intestines is to absorb nutrients from the food we eat. It is not surprising that while some alcohol is absorbed into the bloodstream in the mouth, throat, esophagus, and stomach, the intestines absorb most of it—about 80 percent—into our bodies. Among those who have been drinking heavily over a period of time, alcohol appears to interfere with the ability of the small intestine to absorb certain nutrients (particularly sodium, water, and chloride) even if the diet is well-balanced. This can result in diarrhea, which itself reduces the absorption of nutrients.

It is unclear exactly how alcohol interferes with absorption in the intestines. One possibility is that the body takes the enzymes it would otherwise use to absorb the nutrients and reassigns them to handle the alcohol. Whatever the explanation, this absorption deficiency seems to clear up when the drinker stops drinking.

Alcohol and the Liver

In general, the alcohol absorbed into the body travels to the liver in a system of blood vessels called the *portal system* of veins. As we mentioned before, the liver can handle only so much alcohol at a time. If it is overloaded, it can begin to suffer damage.

There are three general types of liver disorders related to excess alcohol consumption. The first is usually called *fatty liver*, which is believed to develop in the following way. The body "burns" as much fat as it needs in order to produce energy. The liver plays a part in this process. The more alcohol the liver has to break down, the more alcohol and its byproducts (such as hydrogen) are available for the body to "burn" for energy. The less the body has to rely on fat for energy, the more fat accumulates in the liver. Hence, the name "fatty liver."

The second and more serious disorder of the liver is called *alcoholic hepatitis*. This is an inflammation of the liver, and it is a direct result of the damage that prolonged excessive drinking has caused.

The third and most serious of the three liver disorders is *alcoholic cirrhosis*. Cirrhosis is a disease characterized by hardening of portions of the liver. Cirrhosis of the liver can occur from a variety of causes, but in alcoholic cirrhosis, damage to the liver is due to the combination of the alcohol and poor nutrition, not to the alcohol alone. By itself, alcoholic cirrhosis is a particularly damaging disease because it destroys the function of the liver as it progresses.

Of equal importance is the relationship of this liver disease to cancer of the liver. For some reason which is not yet entirely clear, a relationship exists between liver cancer and alcoholic cirrhosis but not between this cancer and other types of cirrhosis.

Alcohol and the Pancreas

The pancreas is a small organ which is situated behind the stomach and attached on one end to the duodenum, the first part of the intestine. The pancreas produces two important fluids. One is insulin, which regulates the body's use of sugar. The other is pancreatic enzyme, which is sent to the duodenum where it aids in the digestion of food.

Prolonged heavy drinking is sometimes associated with *pancreatitis*, a painful condition in which the pancreas becomes inflamed, and with *pancreatic insufficiency*, a condition in which the function of the pancreas is impaired. There is, in addition, some evidence linking pancreatic cancer with prolonged heavy drinking.

Alcohol and the Heart

Alcohol seems to have several effects on the heart. In comparatively low doses (maybe two to four drinks per day), alcohol can increase heart rate and heart output and raise blood pressure slightly. Prolonged heavy use of alcohol can raise blood pressure substantially. Intoxicated individuals can experience irregular heartbeats, even if they are not regular heavy drinkers. The so-called "holiday heart syndrome" is one example. It appears after heavy periods of drinking—say over a weekend or holiday—even in people with no heart disease.

There are two important types of heart disease. One, sometimes called *coronary heart disease* and sometimes *coronary artery disease*, is characterized by blockages of the blood vessels that supply blood to the heart muscle. Coronary heart disease often results in heart attacks. Alcohol does not appear to increase the risk that a person will have a heart attack. In fact, there is some evidence to suggest the opposite—that in *moderate* amounts, alcohol may even help *prevent* heart attacks.

The second important type of heart disease is called *cardimyopathy*. This is a general term for diseases of the heart muscle itself. It is characterized by an enlarged, flabby heart. Research evidence suggests that cardimyopathy occurs more frequently among people who have been drinking heavily for a long time than it does among those who have not been heavy drinkers. It may begin with a decrease in the heart muscle's pumping ability caused by alcohol.

Alcohol and the Body's Muscles

In moderate amounts, alcohol does not seem to have much direct effect on muscles. When people occasionally exceed the amount of alcohol they can tolerate at one time, they may begin to notice a loss of control of some of their muscles. This problem is usually related to alcohol's effect on the brain and how it sends messages to the muscles.

The story, though, may be different for people who

drink heavily over a longer period of time. Prolonged heavy drinking can contribute to a condition called *myopathy*, a disease of the body's muscles. A flareup of this disease may be accompanied by muscle cramps, weakness, and pain. In its more severe and longer-lasting form, some muscles— particularly in the legs—may start to waste away. While myopathy in general can be related to nutritional disorders, myopathy in heavy drinkers is likely due directly to the alcohol itself.

ALCOHOL AND NUTRITION

Earlier we looked for alcohol's nutritional value and found none. Alcohol is empty of nutrition and high in calories—so high, in fact, that heavy drinkers often meet their caloric needs *solely* from the alcohol they drink.

This has not always been the case. The alcoholic beverages produced in earlier times—particularly in early Greek and Roman societies—and the beverages produced today in some other countries have not been robbed of all their nutrients. The nutrients in most beverages produced in the industrialized countries of the world have been stripped away in the process of brewing and distilling the drinks. In fact, not only do alcoholic beverages not have any nutrients to speak of, but also they interfere with the body's ability to absorb nutrients from other foods.

Indirectly, alcohol can have other effects on nutrition. If drinking irritates the stomach and gastritis develops, drinkers lose their appetites and eat less food. When this happens, they take in fewer nutrients. This, combined with the body's inability to absorb whatever they *do* eat during times of heavy drinking, usually leads to one thing: Heavy drinkers are malnourished.

Malnutrition—the absence of proper nutrients from the diet—may, in turn, have important effects on the body. It may be related to changes in mental functions, to blood disorders, to disorders of the nervous system, and to problems with each important part of the body as the nutrients they need become scarcer and scarcer.

ALCOHOL AND THE UNBORN

The effects of alcohol on the unborn fetus of a drinking mother have received an increasing amount of attention lately. As it turns out, alcohol has important effects on the unborn.

When alcohol enters a mother's body, it also enters the body of her unborn child. The problem is that the mother, with her fully-developed liver, can handle the alcohol. Her baby cannot. The liver of the fetus is not as well developed, and it may take the fetal liver twice as long to get rid of the alcohol. So the fetus is bathed in alcohol for a considerably longer time than is the mother's body.

The problem is that as the alcohol moves around the developing fetus it can significantly affect the development of the baby's body. Depending on the stage of fetal development at which the alcohol arrives, how much there is, and how long it stays, the effects it has on the fetus can vary. If it has no effect, the baby is in luck. It can, however, dramatically disrupt the baby's development. Although the effects may vary, taken together, they have been discovered often enough to be designated by a special term—the *fetal alcohol syndrome*, or FAS.

FAS babies tend to be underdeveloped physically, mentally, and emotionally. They are generally smaller, lighter, and tend to develop more slowly than average babies. Sometimes they have visible physical abnormalities.

No one is sure at present about the amount of alcohol a pregnant woman needs to drink to endanger her unborn baby. It is believed that the fetus will be in danger if its mother drinks more than two drinks a day. But we don't know if there is a "safe" amount of alcohol that a mother can drink. Equally unclear at present is whether different patterns of drinking—say, occasional drinks, or periodic binges, or constant but more moderate drinking—have different effects on fetal development. And it is not clear whether drinking during different phases of pregnancy will affect the fetus differently.

FAS is believed to be the third most common cause of birth defects. It is the number one *preventable* cause of birth defects. About the only certain thing we can say about it at this point is that women can prevent it by not drinking during pregnancy. (In an interesting development, the New York City Council recently passed an ordinance requiring taverns to post a notice informing pregnant women of the dangers alcohol poses for their unborn babies.)

ALCOHOL AND OTHER DRUGS

We'll end this section with some notes on mixing alcohol with other drugs. In a word, *they don't mix*, and the combination can be very unhealthy.

Certain drugs on the market affect the central nervous system, as does alcohol. When they are taken together, it is very possible that each drug—the medication you take and the alcohol you drink—will exaggerate the effect of the other. This can produce effects on the body that are greater than you would expect from combining two drugs with relatively mild individual effects. The combination of their effects is greater than the sum total of their individual actions on the body.

In some cases, combining alcohol and drugs can be very unhealthy. But in those cases in which the combined action of the drugs suppresses certain functions of the body—particularly of the heart and lungs—the reaction can be *deadly*. For this reason, the best advice from the medical authorities is not to mix the two. If you drink, avoid other drugs; if you take other drugs, don't drink.

What is clear is that alcohol is a potent drug that can have profound and long-lasting effects on the human body. Drinkers who suffer alcohol-related symptoms notice the effects, both in the short run and as drinking becomes heavier and more chronic. This suggests two questions: First, why do some people who drink develop drinking problems while others do not? And, second, if alcohol can do all these things to us and we know about them, why do some people continue to drink so much?

Chapter 2

What Is Alcoholism, Anyway?

Consider this formula: 5 oz. wine = 12 oz. beer = 3 oz. sherry/port wine = 1 1/2 oz. whiskey = 1 cocktail. What the different amounts of these different drinks have in common is that they contain equal amounts of *alcohol*.

WHAT IS ALCOHOL?

Actually, there is a whole family of chemicals called "alcohols." It is important here to distinguish between *alcohol* and *beverage alcohol*. Beverage alcohol is the particular member of the family of alcohols known as *ethanol*. We find other members of the family of alcohols in many products we buy, and they are very poisonous.

Beverage Alcohol

Beverage alcohol—ethanol—has long been known for its ability to intoxicate. Wine, for example, is mentioned more than 500 times in the Bible. The Egyptians attributed the invention of beverage alcohol to one goddess, the Romans to another. Beer was well-known in Ancient Sumeria as early as 6000 B.C. In fact, it was likely present before written historical records appeared.

The passage of time expanded the variety of available beverage alcohol. Distilled spirits, with their higher alcohol content, were introduced to Europeans in the eleventh century—two centuries or so after the process of distillation was discovered in what is now the Middle East.

One distilled beverage, gin, plays a very important role in the history of alcohol abuse and its prevention. Distilled first in Holland, gin led to a major social upheaval as it was consumed in excess by England's poor as a way to help them forget their poverty. As a result, it was the focus of one of the first organized efforts by a society to control the abuse of alcohol by its citizens.

Attempts to control "drunkenness" in England began in the sixteenth century, when it first became a crime. Gin was the target of two "Gin Acts" in the eighteenth century and the focus of riots and continuing social unrest as its production and consumption rose for a century.

As was to be the experience in the United States 200 years later, each attempt at prohibition was met by the production of bootleg gin, much of it of inferior quality and some of it deadly poison.

Alcohol in America

In early seventeenth century Colonial America, drinking and drunkenness were already recognized problems. Over the next 100 years, a series of legislative moves in several colonies sought to restrict, regulate, and define the legitimate sale and use of beer, wine, and spirits, even in the home. As early as 1671, the symptoms of what we now call "alcoholism" had already been spelled out in colonial laws.

The use and abuse of alcohol was the subject of debate and legislation all over America for the next century. As the abuse of alcohol rose, so did efforts to control it. Official actions included the establishment of laws and assessments of fines and punishments for public inebriates and those who permitted or aided their intoxication.

At the same time, a series of temperance societies sprang up. These groups were organized for a single purpose: to discourage the consumption of alcohol in any form and to promote sobriety. While the societies were weak at first, it was Benjamin Rush, known as the father of both American medicine and American psychiatry, whose 1785 book *Inquiry into the Effects of Ardent Spirits on the Human Body and Mind* served as the rallying point for the fledgling temperance movement. Fifty years later, these societies were to reach their greatest prominence as society attempted to control what was by then a traditional acceptance of excessive drinking.

Temperance and Prohibition

The temperance movements of the early nineteenth century sowed the seeds of the later prohibition movements. The most famous of these was the national Era of Prohibition, which began in January of 1920, following ratification of the Eighteenth Amendment by the required 36 states. Its goal was to prohibit the production, distribution, and consumption of legitimate beverage alcohol in an attempt to control its use.

But this was not the first such attempt. Support for prohibition of alcohol began to build in the mid-1800s. It gained supporters who formed organizations such as the Prohibitionist Party in 1869 and the Women's Christian Temperance Union (WCTU) shortly thereafter. As a result of pressure from such groups, in 1870 the United States Congress considered the first prohibition amendment to the Constitution. It did not pass. But the supporters did not give up and, led by the groups mentioned above, they continued to lobby for prohibition legislation. By 1910 several state legislatures had passed prohibition laws. By 1932 national political sentiment had turned against prohibition, and it was repealed by passage of the Twenty-first Amendment shortly after the election of Franklin Delano Roosevelt.

Prohibition's legacy is variously described as counterproductive to its avowed goals and as destructive of subsequent attempts to influence the nation's drinking habits. Alcohol abuse not only survived but may have *flourished* during Prohibition's tenure. It was shortly after Prohibition's repeal in 1933 that Alcoholics Anonymous was founded to help those whose abuse had exceeded acceptable bounds.

WHAT IS ALCOHOLISM?

Alcoholism is a term that is frequently used in connection with the abuse of alcohol and its detrimental effects on people's emotional and physical health. However, it has not been defined in such a way that we can point to a group of specific behaviors and symptoms and say, "This is alcoholism."

In many ways, the serious study of alcoholism is still in its infancy. We know only a little bit about the many drinking problems that are variously lumped together and called alcoholism. We would like to be able, for example, to explain why some people develop alcohol problems and other people do not. Unfortunately, we do not really know.

What we suspect is that we will not discover only *one* explanation. The explanations probably lie in several areas. In fact, some people refer to alcoholism in the plural, as the alcoholisms.

For some, it may be that *genetics* are at work. There is research to suggest that some people develop drinking problems because their bodies metabolize alcohol abnormally. Other research in this vein has studied genetically similar individuals—twins—who have been raised in separate homes. Studying these people in this way allows researchers to estimate how genetic components influence drinking habits under conditions in which twins cannot learn drinking habits in the same family. The results of that research suggest that drinking may have a genetic component for some people. In general, genetic contributions are thought to involve biological functions of the body and are likely triggered after a drinking episode starts.

Other researchers have investigated a second possible explanation of drinking problems. They focus not on what happens *after* drinking has started but on what happens *before*. They have looked for *psychological* influences on drinking.

In this and subsequent chapters we will discuss the psychological mechanisms that help maintain abusive drinking patterns. In so doing, we are not suggesting that genetic components are unimportant. Indeed, they may well be very important. However, we are not sure what they may be, and we have little influence on changing them. We can influence our *behavior*—and drinking *is* a behavior—much more easily.

The first point to make here is that, for most drinkers, drinking behavior does not differ substantially from other behaviors. That may seem to be a strange statement to make, but we are talking here about fundamentals. Even though it may be very destructive, drinking behavior follows the same fundamental rules as other behavior, and it can be understood by applying some well-developed psychological principles of behavior.

In general, definitions of drinking behavior have not been successful in creating clear and distinct categories of drinkers. For example, it is not clear to most people how "heavy drinking" differs from "social drinking" or from "problem drinking." Nor is it clear where "problem drinking" ends and "alcoholism" begins. There have been many attempts to define drinking behaviors and problems in a clear and concise manner.

Official Diagnosis of Alcoholism

The official diagnosis of alcoholism is made according to the 1987 Revision of the Third Edition of the American Psychiatric Association's *Diagnositc and Statistical Manual of Mental Disorders*, the so-called "DSM-IIIR." We shall mention the applicable parts of the DSM-IIIR as we discuss diagnosing drinking problems. Please refer to DSM-IIIR for additional information.

Diagnoses can be made along a continuum of four categories. The categories are arranged in order of the severity of the drinking problem and its consequences.

Diagnoses of Alcohol Use and Its Consequences

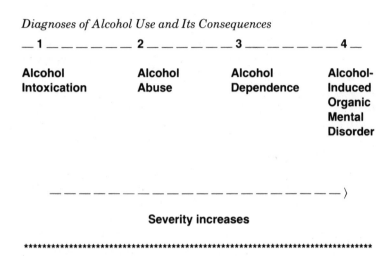

—1 ———————	2 ———————	3 ———————	4 —
Alcohol Intoxication	**Alcohol Abuse**	**Alcohol Dependence**	**Alcohol-Induced Organic Mental Disorder**

— — — — — — — — — — — — — — — — — — — ⟩

Severity increases

****

Alcohol Intoxication describes an acute and relatively brief state in which a person suffers from the effects of drinking too much alcohol. Although an intoxicated person might suffer injury or inflict injury on others during a period of intoxication, the condition itself might do no permanent harm to the person.

Alcohol Abuse is the next category of diagnosis. It addresses a person's drinking *behavior*, rather than just the immediate effects of an episode of drinking. An Alcohol Abuser is defined as a person whose drinking pattern meets three criteria. First, the drinking is maladaptive in one or both of two ways: Either the person drinks continually despite knowing he has a persistent or recurrent social, occupational, psychological or physical problem that is caused or made worse by the drinking, or he repeatedly drinks in situations in which use is physically hazardous. An example of the latter would be the person who drinks and drives.

Second, the maladaptive drinking pattern must have persisted for at least a month, or it must have occurred repeatedly over a longer period of time.

Third, the Alcohol Abuser's drinking pattern must not fit the criteria for the next category of drinking, Alcohol Dependence.

Alcohol Dependence describes a drinking pattern that is more serious than Alcohol Abuse. Two categories of criteria apply to this diagnosis. The first category contains nine items, three of which must apply to the person:

- ☐ The person drinks more, or over a longer period of time, than he intended.
- ☐ The person has a persistent desire, or he has made one or more unsuccessful attempts, to cut down or control the drinking.
- ☐ The person spends a great deal of time getting his beverage, drinking, or recovering from the effects of drinking.
- ☐ The person is frequently intoxicated or suffering from withdrawal symptoms (see below) when expected to fulfill important obligations at work, home, or school or when drinking is physically hazardous (e.g., drinking and driving).
- ☐ The drinker gives up or curtails important social, occupational, or recreational activities because of his drinking.
- ☐ The person drinks continually despite knowing he has a persistent or recurrent social, occupational, psychological, or physical problem that is caused or made worse by the drinking.
- ☐ The person needs markedly increased amounts of alcohol to get drunk or to get the desired effect, or he experiences less and less effect after continually drinking the same amount.
- ☐ The person experiences characteristic withdrawal effects, such as uncontrollable shaking; nausea or vomiting; excessive sweating; racing heartbeat; increased blood pressure; headache; inability to sleep; weakness; seeing, hearing, or feeling things that are not actually there; unrealistic thoughts, such as being pursued by others; or seizures.
- ☐ The person often drinks to relieve or avoid the withdrawal symptoms described above.

The second category for diagnosing Alcohol Dependence is that the symptoms must have persisted at least a month, or they must have occurred repeatedly over a longer period of time.

The last—and most severe—diagnosis of drinking problems covers the long-lasting physical damage to the brain and other vital organs caused by drinking too much for too long. "Too much" and "too long" are individual descriptions. Not everyone's body reacts in the same way to the effects of alcohol. Some people's brains are damaged first; for others it is their livers; still others their hearts, and so on.

For some, drinking relatively little for a relatively short time can cause damage. Others can drink much more over an extended period of time and sustain little damage. Damage can vary from mild to severe, but usually it is not reversible. Peter, a drinker you will meet in the next chapter, is someone who suffered profound damage after an extended career of very heavy drinking.

You will not have to diagnose the drinking pattern that concerns you in the formal categories which the DSM-IIIR provides. In fact, we do not present the information about these categories with the expectation that you will become an expert diagnostician. Let us consider some more straightforward working definitions of drinking problems that may be helpful in your attempt to describe the drinking problem which concerns you.

Working Definitions

Consider these working definitions of drinking behaviors:

Moderate Drinker. This type of drinker is one who drinks occasionally or who drinks a relatively small amount of alcohol with some regularity. People who have a cocktail before dinner or wine with their meal fall into this category.

Heavy Drinker. This a person who drinks every day for at least a year. In addition, every week or two during the year, a heavy drinker will drink more than six drinks at one time. An important part of the definition of heavy drinking is that *no problems are expected* as a result of the drinking.

Problem Drinker. This type of drinker drinks at least as much as the heavy drinker, but problem drinkers also report that drinking has caused problems in their lives. Problem drinking may include getting drunk often, going on frequent "binges" or "benders," or driving while drunk. It may also include drinking to deal with life's pressures and disappointments. Often, problem drinkers do things while drunk that they would never do if sober. But the problem drinker has not crossed the line that separates problem drinking from alcoholism.

Alcoholism. A person crosses the line between problem drinking and *alcoholism* when problems related to his drinking become more specific and less general. Specifically, in order for alcoholism to characterize a person's drinking, problems must be evident in at least three of the following four categories:

1. *The person seems to have lost control of his drinking*. Once he has started, he does not think he can stop. For some, this includes drinking first thing in the morning.

2. *Friends and family members have disapproved of the person's drinking*, and this disapproval may have interfered with the relationships which the drinker has with those people. The drinker may have lost friends, and his marriage may be in trouble. The family's life is frequently disrupted.

Everyone in the family suffers when drinking becomes a problem. In addition to the money he spends on drinking, the drinker may threaten part of the family's livelihood by placing his job in jeopardy. His unpredictability, volatility, broken promises, and excuses probably have become embarrassments for children and adults alike. Along with financial insecurity can come social insecurity and instability. You cannot count on him because you never know what he will do. His children may begin to respond to the constant uncertainty by acting out in school, or by becoming uncharacteristically angry and aggressive or passive and depressed. In many families, members are outraged at the amount of attention the drinker commands by his antics. He intrudes on the family's life, and he antagonizes family members by reducing the family's existence to a shambles.

3. *The drinker has experienced trouble outside the family.* An employer may have warned him about his drinking, or he may have been fired. He may have been arrested for driving under the influence of alcohol or had a run-in with the police for other alcohol-related incidents.

4. *The drinker has experienced physical symptoms related to drinking.* These go beyond an occasional hangover. He may have experienced body tremors, strange thoughts (hallucinations), or seizures. He may lose his memory about drinking episodes. These memory lapses, commonly called *blackouts*, seem to be associated only with either prolonged heavy drinking or individual episodes of heavy alcohol consumption. If they happen with any frequency, it is a strong indication that a person has been drinking too much for too long.

Perhaps a convenient summary working definition of a problem drinker is a person who becomes intoxicated too often in his own view or in the view of his family or friends, or who drives or comes to work while drunk, or who develops medical problems or injuries as a result of his drinking, or who turns to alcohol to cope with problems in his life, or for whom alcohol is a "release" which allows him to "act like a completely different person." When these criteria are related directly to persistent abuse of alcohol, the drinker has an alcohol problem.

CONCEPTS OF ALCOHOLISM

Historically, society's views of drinkers have varied. Colonial American abusers were seen as misfits; they were shunned for their inability to conform to the moral code of the times. Drunken behavior was seen as weakness and continued misuse as a voluntary affront to the prevailing standards of moral and ethical behavior. People with serious drinking problems were thought to be sinners or people without morals who drank because they wanted to. They were generally seen as outcasts who required punishment rather than help. For quite a while, it was a crime to be intoxicated in public, even if a person had not caused any actual harm to property or other people and even if the person had not broken any other laws. In some states, such statutes remain in effect.

Those who hold this moral view of alcoholism might say that drinking becomes a problem because the drinker lacks the "willpower" to stop drinking. In this view, drinking to excess results from a moral deficiency that drinkers could resolve "if only they wanted to."

The moral view of alcoholism may ring true. Some of us may have had to deal with the feelings we have grown up with that heavy drinkers are "weak" people or, perhaps, that they are "immoral."

With the passage of time, and after a number of false starts, the prevailing opinion of drinking problems began to shift. Problem drinkers began to be seen as victims of a disease rather than perpetrators of morally reprehensible acts. That view has become increasingly popular since its latest reintroduction half a century ago. The disease model stresses the involuntary character of abuse problems and suggests a biological basis for misuse of alcohol.

Those who view alcoholism as a disease think of it as a disorder of the body which requires treatment in much the same way that, say, diabetes and chronic heart disease require treatment. In this view, alcoholism develops through no fault of the drinker, except that his drinking has contributed to its development. Treatment of the disease, though, must actively involve the drinker. He must recognize that he has the disease and must work to stop drinking and remain sober.

In this view, drinking triggers further progression of the disease. Sobriety arrests it. There is no permanent cure. The goal of treatment is to "not drink."

However, unlike most physical diseases, each person suffering from this disease may not experience all symptoms thought to characterize it, and it is difficult to identify a common part or organ of the body to which the development of alcoholism can be traced.

Recently, however, a second shift has occurred in conceptualizing drinking and other problems of abuse. Just as the disease orientation supplanted the moralist perception of alcoholism, so have behavioral explanations of such abuse recently encroached on the disease orientation. Behavioral analyses of substance abuse behaviors provided data to support a *psychological* explanation of alcoholism as well. This will be our orientation for the rest of the book.

Those who embrace this psychological concept believe alcoholism develops—and recurs—when drinkers use alcohol to deal with tension, or reduce fears, or escape problems and unpleasant feelings. In this view, alcoholism may be the result when a person chronically turns to alcohol to cope with pressures or frustrations for which he sees no other solutions. From this view, the goal of alcoholism treatment is not merely to stop drinking, but to learn more effective ways to deal with the problems for which alcohol was the former solution.

We can begin to think about abusive drinking by looking to the psychological preparation for drinking that problem drinkers undergo, a preparation of which initially the drinker need not necessarily be aware. His first awareness that something is going on may only come either just before or just after drinking begins. To understand the initial and continued attraction of alcohol, we can look first to what problem drinkers expect alcohol to do for them.

WHAT DO PEOPLE EXPECT FROM ALCOHOL?

The list is pretty long, but we can hit some highlights. Some people expect it to help them be more aggressive, or to help them be aroused sexually more easily, or to be less nervous around other people. It is not surprising in this regard that common themes in television advertisements for beer and wine include references to camaraderie, group activity, and relaxation. These are just the sorts of things that give rise to—or confirm—the expectations drinkers have about the effect their favorite drink will have on them.

Interestingly, there is some research which has shown that people who expect a certain effect will drink more of a beverage when they think it has alcohol in it, regardless of whether it actually does or not, if the taste and smell can be hidden in a mixer, and they experience that effect after drinking a beverage they think has alcohol in it, even if it does not. Pretty strong stuff, these expectations.

Many problem drinkers look to alcohol to *remove* certain unpleasant feelings that otherwise make them feel uncomfortable. It is the *expectation* that the alcohol will *take away* these feelings that lures some people over and over again, even in the face of psychological and physical damage.

People who do not have alcohol problems do not usually drink in the hope that alcohol will take anything away. They tend to drink because the occasion calls for it, and they tend not to overdo it. They have other ways to deal with unpleasant feelings when they arise.

The suggestion here is that, under stress, some people have ways to cope and others do not. Some without other ways to cope turn instead to alcohol for help—in part because it increases their confidence that they can keep things under control.

But alcohol does not really help, even though it may *seem* to when the drinker is intoxicated and his judgment is impaired. Indeed, it usually causes more problems than it solves.

Now, if alcohol doesn't help and if it even makes things *worse*, it may not seem sensible to suggest, as we have, that people drink because somehow they still *expect* it to do all these things for them. Surely they would learn otherwise from their drinking experiences. Right?

Well, not necessarily. If people have not learned new

ways to cope, they turn to the tried-and-true ways. And alcohol is very familiar for many people.

This is an important point to pursue because if people initially turn to alcohol to do something for them, regardless of whether or not it does it at a cost to their health and well-being that they are willing to pay, then they can learn and choose new, more effective ways to cope with problems.

From the psychological perspective, then, we may be able to construct a partial answer to the question with which we began. It is that people who develop problems with alcohol may differ from those who do not in that they have developed and maintained certain beliefs about what alcohol will do for them, and they have not learned sufficiently how to analyze their behavior and find helpful new ways to handle their problems.

PART 2
What Drinkers Can Do

Chapter 3

Finding Alternatives

Alcoholism affects different people in different ways. Here are four examples.

Jerry

Jerry woke up in the hospital and looked around the room. He wondered to himself, "How did I end up here?" as he guided himself to the door, and "How am I going to get off this merry-go-around of drinking?"

As a first step, he decided to stay in the hospital and get some treatment. Soon he found himself talking to counselors about work problems, arguments with his wife and children, and scrapes with the law which had accompanied his drunken episodes over the years. He could recall quite well how drinking at first had been fun for him and how his reputation grew as his capacity for liquor increased. But that had changed, and now he had to clean up the damage that the drinking had done.

What became evident during treatment in the hospital became painfully obvious to Jerry when he left the hospital. Things had changed in his family over the years when he drank heavily. He now felt like a boarder in his own home. Since his paycheck had gone for his liquor, his wife had gotten a job and had been functioning independently for a number of years. Financially and emotionally, she did not rely on him. Further, he discovered that, while his children tolerated him, they did not respect his authority. They, too, had adjusted their lives to a drunken father on whom they could not rely.

Jerry continued his treatment at the hospital's outpatient clinic in a therapy group that helped him continue his adjustment to sobriety. His family also came to the clinic and, with the help of a counselor, began to work out the problems that remained after Jerry stopped drinking.

It has been three years since they completed family counseling. Jerry is still sober, the family has accepted him back as a full member, and both Jerry and his wife share the responsibilities of running the household and raising the children.

Peter

Peter's case is a lot more complicated. He was an officer in the armed forces who had attended one of the service academies and later taught there. He had the reputation of being one of the brightest and toughest officers in the service, and he rose steadily through the ranks. He was married and had two children. He also drank heavily for many years, although to this day he denies that his drinking has ever been a problem. As we shall see, it was.

When he first entered treatment for his drinking, Peter was articulate and spent a lot of his energy tending to his outward appearance. He seemed somewhat glib to staff members when talking about problems in his life. His wife visited him every day during this first hospitalization. She did not agree with staff members that he had a drinking problem, but said that it probably would not be a bad idea if he toned down his drinking. Both presented the picture of a model family. When he left the hospital, he declined any continuing counseling.

By the time of his second admission, less than one year later, Peter's performance in the service had declined markedly, and he had been demoted in rank. His behavior had become intolerable to his superiors. He had been absent frequently and prone to emotional outbursts with his colleagues. His superiors had threatened him with early retirement if he did not stop drinking, but that warning had not led to improvement. When he was admitted to the hospital, he appeared much more deteriorated physically. He had been a husky man, but now he had lost a good deal of his muscle tone and showed physical signs of deterioration. His skin was rough and blotchy, his face was ruddy and covered with red lines, and his posture was rather sloppy. At this point, both Peter and his wife still refused to link his problems to his drinking, but his wife did volunteer that he had become physically violent, had beaten and kicked her at times and, at least on one occasion, had broken a couple of her ribs.

In the next 12 months, Peter was admitted to the hospital twice for treatment of alcohol-related problems. The first time was after he had stopped drinking for two days and had been frightened by some strange experiences. He had seen several bugs scurrying around his living room floor which would disappear when he looked at them directly. He also had seen a very large squirrel pop out of one wall and then disappear behind a chair. This experience was so real to him that he went over to the chair to look for a hole in the wall. When he found none, he then reasoned that the squirrel must be hiding in the wall, and he knocked a hole in the wall to look for it. After one day in the hospital, these visions stopped. He had started to "dry out."

During Peter's third admission in two years, his physician told him that he had done major damage to his liver and other organs as a result of his drinking and that if he did not stop drinking, he would very likely develop a number of life-threatening complications. When his wife was told of this, she admitted privately to the social worker that Peter had a drinking problem. However, she would admit this only if he was not in the room with her. And, although she had desperately pleaded for Peter's admission to the hospital when he was drinking, her attitude changed once he was admitted. She suddenly saw no need for him to make any major changes. Instead, she went regularly to church to pray for divine intervention.

By the following year—three years after his first admission—Peter had been forcibly retired from the service. He had been admitted to the hospital once again, much more confused mentally. Often he did not realize where he was, or know the date (or even the season) or recognize his visitors. He was deteriorated physically to the point that he appeared emaciated. When he talked to others, he often did not make sense and was very distant emotionally. On three occasions when he was released from the hospital for short home visits, he became violent with his wife, refused to return to the hospital, and had to be brought back by the police. A year and a half later, the length of his fourth admission, he was transferred to a long-term geriatric care center, where he remains today.

Linda

Linda had worked for a well-known local law firm for ten years. She can remember when she first began to drink regularly. It was while she was in college, and she drank because it helped her socialize with men. That is the reason most of her friends drank, and it worked for her. Now the urge to drink was increasing as her boss gave her more and more work. Her drinking increased markedly. She began to make mistakes that were costly for her firm, and she was suspended after three ineffective warnings about her drinking. At that point, she decided to enter the hospital for treatment.

After four days Linda was "dried out," and she elected to continue her treatment as an outpatient. During her treatment, she was able to identify two important aspects to her drinking. First, she often drank in order to relieve the tension she felt both at work and when she socialized with other people. Second, she felt tense because she had trouble living up to what she thought other people expected of her. As a result, she took on an increasing number of tasks until she had more than she could handle. By the time she realized what had happened, she had become tense and angry. At that point she thought alcohol was the best alternative for her to turn to for relief of her tension.

Once she discovered these two things about herself, she learned ways to overcome them. She learned to relieve tension by using the specific relaxation techniques taught to her in treatment. She also learned to set limits on herself and to decline others' requests if they exceeded those limits. She learned to say "no." She had identified the types of feelings that told her she was in a "high risk" situation which could lead her again to drink too much, and she learned what to do when she felt those feelings—*before* they got out of hand. She learned to be "on guard." Five months later, after three months back on the job, Linda said she felt less pressure and was speaking up when the load was too great. And she had not returned to drinking.

Sue

Sue had been drinking heavily for 15 years when she came for treatment. She had not lost her job, although she had been cautioned by her supervisor about her drinking. But her husband and children had become increasingly disturbed about her behavior at home. She spent most of her time at home alone after work and on weekends, usually drinking. "Mornings after" were particularly hard because they tended to upset the family from the very start of the day. So she entered the hospital for treatment.

Treatment went well for Sue. She learned a lot about her drinking and about the effect of alcohol on her body. In addition, her family eagerly participated in treatment with her during her hospitalization. As discharge approached, both she and her family were optimistic about their future together. And with good reason; the treatment had been very helpful at a time when the family life seemed to be falling apart.

Sue returned to work shortly after she was discharged from the hospital. Both Sue and her family continued in outpatient treatment, and Sue attended AA meetings.

One Wednesday afternoon several months later, Sue's children returned from school to find her at home. She had been sent home from work because she had been drinking.

Apparently, it had taken her supervisor a few days to discover that Sue was drinking again. It was a shock to her family; they had not suspected it either. When her husband arrived home, the family sat down with Sue and expressed their feelings of disappointment. They told her they wanted to discuss her slip with their counselor.

Initially, Sue balked at the idea. She said, "I don't want to go back. The treatement obviously isn't helping me." When Sue's husband and children talked it over among themselves, they decided to continue in treatment, even if Sue did not continue with them. They told Sue, "You may not think it's helpful for you, but it is for us." As it turned out, on the day of the appointment, Sue changed her mind and decided to continue coming with her family for counseling. Over the next few sessions, Sue and her family weathered the crisis of her slip.

GETTING HELP

These four people have experienced some of the common problems of alcoholism, and each has responded in a different way. Each came for treatment because drinking had caused difficulties for them, but not all became involved in treatment in the same way. Jerry, Linda, and Sue were able to find some answers. Peter never did. What about you—or the person you know who drinks too much? What could *you* do to get things underway?

A common question many people ask is: "Why should I help a problem drinker? He got himself into this mess. Let him get himself out of it." As we can see from the lives of the four people we just met, there are two practical reasons why it may be appropriate to help a problem drinker.

Reason 1: *Prompt treatment minimizes the degree to which alcohol damages the body.* As we discussed earlier, prolonged heavy drinking has very definite negative effects on the drinker's health. By helping stop the drinking promptly, you are practicing preventive medicine, and you may truly be saving the drinker's life. The same applies to his mental health. Prompt treatment may save the drinker's life in this sense as well.

Reason 2: *Prompt attention reduces the amount of social disruption and emotional trauma the drinker and his family suffer.* Loss of jobs, financial debts, domestic violence, and child abuse all accompany alcoholism. It is amazing how much some family members will suffer before anyone takes action on the drinking problem. Thus, prompt treatment for the drinker makes good sense for the drinker, for the drinker's family, and for society in general.

Though it may make good sense to help the problem drinker, it is often hard to do. Drinkers are often considered to be "deadbeats." Many of us have learned to ignore alcoholism in general and to despise problem drinkers in particular. All of us are affected by the prejudices and value judgments we have learned to accept. How many of us have come to accept an image of problem drinkers as "skid row bums" or weak-willed members of our communities? And how many of us feel comfortable talking directly with a drinker about his problem? All of this makes it difficult for us actually to do what makes "good sense." If this is true for those who do not have drinking problems, how much more difficult must it be for those who do? But in both cases, ignoring the problem may, in the long run, be more painful than facing it ever could be. Certainly that was the case with Peter.

This means that we must force ourselves to do something about it. And that means seeking out some sort of treatment. But what? And where? Those who have not yet sought out treatment for their problems may not know very much about it or, for that matter, about the problems themselves. Treatment may conjure up many different images in the minds of those who want help for themselves, for a loved one, or for a friend. Images of "snake pits" or of locked, prison-like buildings holding physically damaged or deranged people are not uncommon. In fact, though, the typical treatment facility—whether hospital or community clinic—is designed for comfort and treatment rather than confinement and punishment.

What Should I Do If I Have a Drinking Problem?

In general, the answer to this question is to *get help.* We know some drinkers who say something like, "I don't need any help. Why, old John Jacobs used to drink a quart a day and just stopped by himself. If he can do it, so can I."

Maybe so, but you have to weigh the odds. Many people *cannot* stop by themselves. It is just like getting from the top of Niagara Falls to the bottom. There are two ways to do it. One is to take the elevator provided to help you down. The other is to do it yourself—go over the Falls in a barrel. There are men who did it and lived, so it is *possible*—but would *you* do it?

Maybe you're saying, "That's a stupid example. Of course I wouldn't. If I went over the Falls in a barrel and failed, I could get killed." Well, if you try to stop drinking on your own and fail, you can kill yourself just as surely. For every John Jacobs, there are many who tried to stop on their own and failed. And failing to stop could be very dangerous for you.

If you decide to seek help, the next questions are "Where?" and "How do I find out what I need?" Generally, these questions can be answered best if you can talk with someone who can help you evaluate the seriousness of your problem. This person may be your family physician. It may also be someone at a local alcohol treatment center.

There are several ways to find out how to contact these types of facilities. Your family physician may be able to refer you to one. Your local, county, or state medical, psychological, or psychiatric society can often help you, or you might also call your local hospital or health department and ask for a referral. Try talking to the hospital's public relations department if you do not know anyone there. Alcoholics Anonymous (AA) may be able to tell you where to find a treatment program as well as provide you with some assistance. (AA phone numbers are listed in the white pages of your phone book, usually under "Alcoholics Anonymous.") You could turn to the state or federal government for help. They publish helpful directories of treatment facilities. We have included a listing at the end of the book of possible sources to contact for referrals to treatment facilities (see Appendix D).

One source of assistance that has become increasingly available is to be found in Employee Assistance Programs, or EAPs. In the last decade it has become clear that every alcohol-abusing employee can cost his employer up to 25 percent more than his salary each year because of the effect alcohol has on his work. In response to this rather startling impact on the workplace, many employers now sponsor programs to help employees deal with their alcohol problems. These programs often hire counselors to work with alcohol-abusing employees and establish AA meetings at work. They also may refer employees to one or more treatment facilities, if they need more intensive treatment than can be provided at the worksite. Your personnel office, union officer, or the company nurse or physician will be able to tell you if your employer sponsors such a program. If so, it is a sign both that your employer encourages his employees to seek help for their alcohol problems and that those who come forward with their problems will likely not be punished. Linda's law firm clearly subscribed to this belief. Once she had received treatment for her problem, her employer reinstated her.

What You Can Expect During and From Treatment?

There is no "average" treatment. People should take care to select the types of treatment which best suit them and their drinking problems. This means that people must learn to choose alcoholism treatment services in the same discriminating way they choose their clothes and other products.

The general goal of treatment for alcohol problems is for you to learn how to get along comfortably in life without needing to use alcohol. This general goal can be accomplished in a variety of ways depending on the nature of your problem. If you need to get rid of the alcohol in your system, you may enter a hospital or community clinic to "dry out." This process—called *detoxification*—is often followed by a *rehabilitation* program lasting from two to four weeks. Other people require less intensive treatment. They may, instead, enter an *outpatient treatment program.* Outpatient treatment can last for a number of months. It typically means that the drinker comes to see a counselor up to 5 times per week at first, followed by less frequent and less intensive treatment. Outpatient treatment is often associated with rehabilitation programs in hospitals and community clinics. For others, attendance at Alcoholics Anonymous meetings alone might be the best treatment.

THE DRINKER'S ROLE IN TREATMENT

In general, treatment of alcohol problems—no matter what the duration—differs from short-term treatment you might have received for some common complaints. If you have been treated by a physician for an infection, the treatment probably centered on the physician. Most likely, you began by describing your symptoms. Your physician examined you and perhaps conducted certain medical tests to pinpoint your problems. Finally, the physician gave you some medication to kill the infection and cure your ailment. Your direct involvement probably consisted totally of your accurate description of the symptoms and your taking medication as prescribed. The physician and the medicine did the rest.

Treatment of alcohol problems requires the drinker to take a good deal more responsibility for resolving his problems. To this extent, treatment of alcoholism resembles the management of long-term medical problems such as diabetes, in which the person suffering from the ailment must remain involved in its treatment long after it is initially evaluated and diagnosed. As we saw with Sue, you can expect to master your drinking problem with proper attention to it, but only with your full involvement in treatment.

Drinking problems have a tendency to recur even after treatment if the drinker ignores other parts of his life that may be related to his drinking.

Drinking History

The first thing that will probably happen when you seek help is that someone will take what is generally called a "drinking history." It is a necessary first step in treatment because it helps you and the interviewer understand your problems past and present, and decide together on the best course of treatment. The "drinking history" can be collected by questionnaire, but it is more likely that it will be gathered in an interview. It generally consists of several types of questions, such as:

- ☐ What is your chief complaint right now?
- ☐ What do you usually drink? (Beer, vodka, wine, etc.)
- ☐ How much do you drink on an average day?
- ☐ How long have you been drinking that amount?
- ☐ When did you have your last drink?
- ☐ When did you start drinking?
- ☐ When did your drinking become a problem?
- ☐ How has your drinking caused problems in your life (at home, work, etc.)?
- ☐ Have you experienced physical symptoms as a result of your drinking? (Pains, shakes, memory lapses, seizures or convulsions, injuries, etc.; has your mind played tricks on you?)
- ☐ Have you been treated by a physician or at a hospital in the past few years?
- ☐ Have you been treated for an alcohol problem before?
- ☐ Why have you come for treatment at this time?
- ☐ What medical problems do you have at this time?

After the drinking history is completed, a decision can be made about the most appropriate type and sequence of treatment for you. For some people, the next step in treatment is detoxification.

Detoxification

If treatment is to proceed effectively, you must first stop drinking and get the alcohol out of your system. This is the process called *detoxification*. It is a time of withdrawal from heavy use of alcohol. The process of detoxification takes place either in a hospital, in a doctor's office, or sometimes in a specially designed non-medical detoxification program.

The best detoxification tool is time. The only way to get alcohol out of the body is to give the liver time to take it out of the blood and break it down. This process might be uncomfortable for you because you could have to put up with some unpleasant effects of withdrawal from alcohol.

If the process of withdrawal is merely uncomfortable, detoxification can be accomplished safely in a non-medical setting. Some places have sobering-up stations that help people "dry out" without the aid of medication, and this can be a safe and very effective way to sober up.

But for some, the process of detoxification is more complicated. Some people have consumed too much alcohol for too long and experience some serious side effects when they stop drinking. For them, medical supervision of their detoxification is a good idea.

Several types of things may happen during detoxification. Because heavy drinkers are often malnourished or dehydrated, they can have serious problems with their central nervous systems. Some have the "shakes" or high blood pressure or rapid heartbeat. They may not be fully aware of what is going on around them, and they can be very anxious. Jerry, for example, was not quite sure how he got there when he woke up in the hospital. Others might have convulsions. In addition, they can also be agitated and experience hallucinations. Hallucinations are tricks the mind plays; people can see things that are not really there (Peter's bugs and his squirrel are good examples) or hear someone talking when no one is around or feel something on their skin when nothing is actually there.

Even more frightening can be the irrational thoughts and feelings that can arise. Some people begin to think, for example, that "everyone is out to get me" or that some vague but terrifying force will do them harm.

These symptoms generally appear—if at all—within three days after drinking stops. They tend to last three days or less. When they do occur, they are serious medical problems that require the care of a physician.

Medical detoxification usually involves close monitoring of the drinker's progress. Medicine is available to help with the agitation and seizures. In severe cases, malnutrition and dehydration can be treated by intravenous feedings. Most often, though, these can be treated effectively by a regular or fortified diet and by drinking plenty of fluids.

The physician makes regular assessments of blood pressure and heart rate, and orders doses of supplemental vitamins. But again, though the medical treatment is important in order to avoid or treat the serious side effects of withdrawal, the best weapon is time—time for the body to get rid of the alcohol and time for it to readjust to functioning without alcohol.

Although some people believe that a person is fully detoxified only after a year or 18 months without drinking, the initial period of detoxification usually lasts from three to seven days. The length of detoxification usually depends on two things: how and to what degree the body has reacted to the overdoses of alcohol.

REHABILITATION TREATMENT

Detoxification deals with the alcohol actually present in the body, and with the major medical complications sometimes associated with withdrawal from alcohol. *Rehabilitation* deals with drinking behavior. It most often focuses on helping people accept the fact that they have a drinking problem, helping them gain insight into the reasons behind their drinking, and offering them forms of treatment that help them cope with life without drinking.

Inpatient Rehabilitation Treatment

Inpatient treatment generally is used first. In the past, inpatient treatment philosophies suggested that the drinker needed to rehabilitate himself over a period of time in a sober, stable environment. Inpatient stays commonly lasted six to eight weeks and often stretched into several months. The trend today, however, is to reduce costly inpatient stays and emphasize follow-up care.

Whatever the type of treatment—inpatient or outpatient—the exact nature of treatment follows from the concept of alcoholism to which the treatment staff subscribes. The treatment program that might result from the concept of alcoholism we discussed earlier would consist of:

Care for Physical Problems

People are usually free from major alcohol-related physical problems requiring medical attention when they enter rehabilitation treatment. Such symptoms as the shakes, strange thoughts, excessive sweating, the extended hangover, and other problems associated with withdrawal from alcohol are resolved during the detoxification phase of treatment. Some physical problems associated with drinking can require treatment as you progress through a rehabilitation program. For example, we have already discussed the effect of prolonged drinking on the body's absorption of nutrients. In order to help your body recover nutritionally from the effects of drinking, rehabilitation treatment usually includes a balanced diet and a continuation of vitamin and mineral supplements. Since it is often the case that drinkers ignore aspects of their physical health when they are drinking, your rehabilitation treatment will likely include a recommendation for an exercise program to help get your body back in physical shape. However, rehabilitation treatment focuses only a small amount of its attention on physical problems. It deals mostly with the other three components of alcoholism.

Education for Social Problems

Alcoholism is a social problem as well as a physical and psychological one. Certainly the person's environment is affected by his drinking—auto accidents result, work productivity declines, bills go unpaid. On the other hand, the person's environment affects his drinking—the Happy Hours, "one for the road," "let's discuss it over a beer." The interactions between a drinker and his environment are often complex. To help you understand them, your rehabilitation program may offer educational seminars. Seminars might be presented in various topics—medical aspects of alcoholism, nutrition, etc. They are intended to present you with some cold, hard facts. The seminars use films, tapes, lectures, and reading materials to make their points.

One form of seminar that seems to be effective focuses both on the social pressures involved in the decisions to drink and stop drinking, and on the factors that lead to a resumption of drinking after treatment. As noted before, no one can make you drink—*you* pick up the glass. But these seminars can help you identify what situations encourage you to drink even when you may not want to. By becoming more aware of these situations, you can learn either to avoid them or to be on your guard if you cannot avoid them.

Psychotherapy for Psychological Problems

The first step in successful treatment will be to control the drinking. Treatment cannot be successful if the drinker continues to drink heavily during treatment. Heavy drinking dulls the senses and prevents a person from participating fully in the treatment process. The process of solving the problems associated with drinking can usually be started only by first stopping the drinking. Once it is stopped, treatment can begin.

Psychotherapy is an integral part of both inpatient and outpatient treatment programs. It is most often conducted in groups, but many treatment centers also offer individual psychotherapy. Its general focus is to help you understand the role alcohol played in your life and to learn what to substitute for it.

Group psychotherapy involves one or two counselors and between seven and ten clients. They sit together in a room—usually at a regularly scheduled time of the day or week—and they talk. Clients talk about themselves— their thoughts and feelings, their problems and their successes—as part of a process through which they, as group members, begin to understand what makes them tick. As they talk, other group members offer their observations in a way that helps each member see how he affects others and how he might change to combat some of his problems. The role of the counselor is to help the group see problems in new ways when it gets "stuck."

Individual and family therapy have the same goals as group therapy, although these therapies take place with one client and one counselor, or with a family and either one or two counselors.

Whether the therapy takes place in a group, alone with a counselor, or with your family, an important thing to keep in mind is that it will take time. You can expect to feel better pretty soon after treatment starts, but you probably will not solve all your problems in a month. It is usually not that simple.

The unfortunate thing is that many people see stopping drinking simply as a test of "willpower," a psychological wrist-wrestling contest. The whole concept of willpower refers back to some old concepts of alcoholism that we discussed earlier.

Outdated concepts of alcoholism attributed prolonged heavy drinking to moral weakness, a lack of "willpower." Where this belief still exists today, it should be based on a complete understanding of the concept of "willpower."

We can think of willpower as a combination of the "will" to do something and the "power" to get it done. Most drinkers come to treatment because they want to stop their drinking or at least control it. There is often no lack of will.

What is missing is the power to stop drinking and stay sober. By "power" we are referring to the ability to translate the will into action. If the drinker is to overcome the problem fully, he first must *understand* the problem. So what people really seem to be referring to is the "power" part of willpower. The role of psychotherapy is to help you develop the power—the tools you need to stay sober—by helping you learn about yourself and the things you need to do differently in your life.

Some heavy drinkers maintain that "drinking is my *only* problem." For some, that might be so. But for many others, it is probably *not* so. Drinking and personal problems seem to go hand in hand. They seem to form a vicious circle. Personal problems can make drinking more attractive, and drinking can make problems worse.

The difficulty with the circle is that it is often hard to know right away which came first. Did your problems contribute to your drinking or did the drinking contribute to your problems? Probably, a little of each has happened, and therefore, both must be addressed in treatment.

At the start, the most obvious thing you can say about your drinking is that it has caused some disturbing consequences. Perhaps your health, job, family relationships, or friendships have suffered. Perhaps you have been in trouble with the law as a result of your drinking. But while it may be that people notice the *consequences* of their drinking at first, it is also true that drinking itself may be a consequence of something that *preceded* it.

Your drinking, then, might not only be a *problem*. It may also be a *solution* for you, even though the problems that might have contributed to it can be difficult to identify.

In general, a person's life has different parts. A person usually has a number of different relationships, and he engages in a number of different activities. Add them all up and you will be able to describe a person's life. For example, family relationships, friendships, leisure-time activities, and a job might be four segments in someone's life.

There are probably more. In drinkers' lives, one of the additional segments is the alcohol they drink. If we draw a drinker's life as a wheel, it might look something like this:

By entering treatment, a drinker has decided to remove the alcohol from his life. But, by doing so, he creates a problem. Removing the alcohol disturbs the wheel. It makes things bumpy until something else can be put in its place to replace the alcohol.

For example, if alcohol plays an important role in a person's life, there can be an awkward period after he stops drinking while he develops new ways to use his leisure time. Clearly, the greater the role alcohol played in his life, the more difficult may be that person's adjustment when he stops drinking.

One way you can learn how to find a replacement for the alcohol is to learn to understand the role it played in your life. Think about the relationship you had with alcohol. Relationships are never one-sided; they usually involve some give and take. Like other relationships, your relationship with alcohol has had some bad consequences and some good consequences. It involves a trade—you got hurt, but you get something in return.

Bear with us for a moment and consider this analogy.

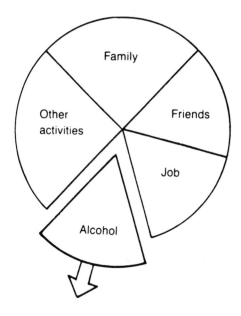

If we gave you a hammer and asked you to whack yourself on the arm as hard as you could, you would probably refuse. In fact, you would likely think we were crazy to make such an absurd request! Why would we expect you to injure yourself? But suppose we gave you the hammer and $20,000 and asked you to whack your arm? Ridiculous, you say? But now you might think about it a bit harder. You might *do* it. Well, your drinking is similar in this respect. You would not do something to yourself that so clearly injures you—like drinking so much so often—unless you got something pretty important in return. You probably didn't get anything as concrete as $20,000, but you got *something*.

Now it is probably true that few people drink heavily because they like the taste of their favorite alcoholic beverage or because they have "always" drunk heavily. Many drinkers say they drink for the "good times." While this might have been true originally for the problem drinker, it is no longer true when physical illness, domestic problems, and difficulty at work are the outcomes. While some people like Peter deny the connection between their drinking and their problems, in most cases it is hard to explain why they continue with such damaging behavior.

Heavy drinkers do not continue their drinking because they enjoy it. They continue drinking because they need it to function.

Because they *need* it? Yes. Drinking is one of a number of alternative solutions to problems of living. For the drinker, it has become the best—or easiest or most familiar—alternative solution to some difficulty. As we said earlier, drinking is similar to most things we do in life in that it carries with it both benefits and costs. Can you begin to think about what you gained from drinking that was important enough to offset all the negative consequences of your drinking? Think of your choice of alcohol in terms of a scale. Your gains from drinking must have equalled or exceeded your losses if you have continued to drink. The scale must stay in balance.

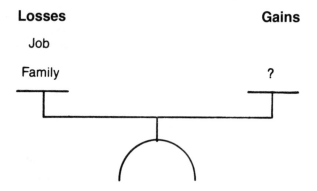

Losses   **Gains**

Job

Family   ?

Now, it might be easy for you to identify those things you have given up in your relationship. The injury is probably all too clear to you. You might have given up your job or your family or your health or your friends or your self-respect or all of these—and maybe more. But what did you get in return? What you took—or got—from your relationship with alcohol is not so easy to figure out.

Perhaps some questions might be helpful. Try asking yourself these:

- [ ] What would be difficult for me in my life if I never drank again, starting right now?
- [ ] What would my life be like if it weren't for my drinking?
- [ ] What would I have to learn (or change) about myself in order to stop drinking and stay sober?
- [ ] What would I have to learn to do differently in my life in order to stay sober?
- [ ] What situations will really test my decision to stay sober?
- [ ] What obstacles will stand between me and sobriety after I have "dried out"?

People constantly face stress in our modern, complex world. But not all people react in the same manner to the situations in which they find themselves. Some cope quite well; others do not. Some of those who do not may develop psychological problems in response to the stress. Others may learn to cope by drinking. Those who have learned to cope by drinking—and you may be among them—can also learn to cope in more effective and less damaging ways. Do not underestimate your capacity to understand and change the relationship of your drinking to the rest of your life.

An important part of alcohol's ability to help people cope is that they expect that it will help them to cope. Researchers have demonstrated that people's behavior changes in difficult situations after having a drink. But behavior also changes when people have a drink that they think has alcohol in it, *even when that drink has no alcohol in it.* As long as people *think* that a drink will help, it most often *will* help, even if they only *believe* they have had an alcoholic drink. To be sure, part of alcohol's effect on behavior is due to its physical effect on the body. But an equal or more important effect on the drinker's behavior may come from the drinker's mind—from his or her thoughts and emotions.

Your answers to the questions above, difficult though they might be, will be a good start in discovering what you need help with in order to stop drinking. The answers can help you identify some objectives for your treatment. For example, you might discover that a big test of your sobriety will be handling anger and frustration when a particularly trying situation comes up. One objective for treatment, therefore, might be to learn to handle the anger and frustration in some other way besides drinking. Or you might discover that social situations can really tempt you to drink. In this case, you might need to learn how to be less shy or how to refuse successfully the drinks others may want you to have. Or . . . well, there are many other possibilities that may apply to you. The main point here is that starting to think about these questions is a good idea. It is crucial to a complete understanding of your drinking problem. And the sooner you start, the sooner your treatment is likely to start having an effect.

Let us consider the possibility that certain specific situations in your life may be related to your drinking. If certain specific situations were related to drinking, could you stop your drinking simply by avoiding those situations? The relationship would look like this:

Consider Charlie, one of Linda's college drinking friends. Charlie began to recognize that his drinking was getting out of hand. He identified two problems related to his drinking: He would drink too much prior to a visit by his in-laws and when needed house repairs accumulated. He decided to solve his problems by inviting his in-laws less frequently and by setting aside Saturday morning for house maintenance chores. However, Charlie noticed that his drinking did not decrease, and he was puzzled.

It is no wonder that Charlie was puzzled. He skipped a step in his thinking. The missing link is the *emotional reactions* we have to various things in our lives and the way we learn to cope with those reactions. In other words, situations *themselves* don't lead people to drink; *reactions* to those situations do. For example, your neighbor might be invited to a party and need a drink to cope with his nervousness before he leaves home. You might not. It is your neighbor's emotional reaction to the situation—the nervousness—rather than the situation itself—the party—that is related to his drinking. After all, in the same situation, you may be fine. Here's the important link:

Taking the example a step further, we can say that your neighbor has learned to cope with the nervousness by drinking. But would it be fair to say that this is the *only* type of situation that makes him nervous? Probably not. And, if not, might other situations that also make him nervous also result in drinking? This extension of the point above might be portrayed more accurately like this:

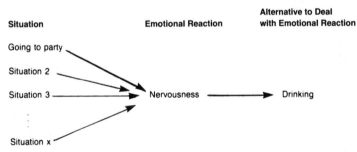

The point of this example is twofold. First, since your drinking is related most directly to your emotional reactions, the most appropriate place to focus your thoughts about treatment is on those reactions. That is what Charlie needed to do and what Linda actually did in treatment. You can remove yourself from a thousand situations, but you cannot remove yourself from your emotions.

Second, we have been assuming so far that drinking is the *one* and only method for coping with problems of living. Obviously, it is not. It is only one of many alternatives from which you could choose. Indeed, you can learn other ways to cope with those difficult emotional reactions.

Remember Linda? In her case, the diagram above is more accurate in this form:

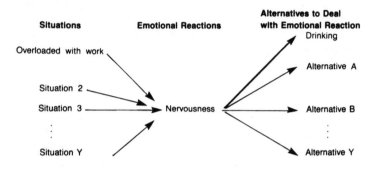

Recall for a moment that scale we talked about earlier. We said that what you got had to equal or exceed what you gave up. What you gave up is clear to you. What you got is a way to cope with one or more emotions that have been difficult for you to handle. With this in mind, let us turn our attention to some ways to help figure out what these could be for you and how to develop other alternatives for dealing with them. Here are two cases to illustrate a helpful method of analysis. (Appendix C is a worksheet to help you use this five-step method to analyze your own situation.)

Two weeks after outpatient treatment started, Linda was at a party for one of her friends. When offered a drink, she found herself ready to accept it. While she ended up refusing the drink, the experience was disturbing to her, and she left the party. She brought this incident up at her next counseling appointment.

In the counseling session she began to review the incident and arrived at the following analysis. First, she recreated the situation in her mind as closely as she could. She recalled being in a room full of people, most of whom were strangers to her. Most people seemed to know each other and were busy in conversation when she arrived. Second, she recalled feeling very tense, and, in her words, "I froze." She could remember many social gatherings in which she had had similar feelings. Third, the warning signs of her tension had been very clear to her. As she went to light her cigarette, she noticed her hands were shaking, and she began to feel "butterflies" in her stomach. Fourth, she realized that her impulse to take a drink was almost automatic. It was this automatic quality that had most concerned her. Someone had offered her a drink just at a moment when she was feeling particularly uncomfortable. It had been her habit in the past to use alcohol to calm herself down. Two or three quick drinks would make her feel more relaxed, but this time she stopped to think of other ways to relax. As she looked back on it, it had taken an active effort for her to resist her past habit to drink.

Fifth, however, although Linda had managed not to drink at the party, she told her counselor that "I don't want to have to leave every party just because I get nervous." Leaving the party was not a very good solution for her, even though it kept her from drinking. She and her counselor turned their attention to some other alternatives, which they worked on in the next several counseling sessions.

The second a person we want to tell you about here is Frank. Frank is a 42-year-old man who has a wife and three children. He is an office manager in the local branch of an insurance company. Over the years, Frank had been known to his co-workers and his family as "a nice guy," one who takes on too much at work. Until the past two years they thought of his drinking sprees as the "T.G.I.F." behavior that characterizes some hard workers. Since then, however, his drinking increased in frequency and quantity so that he began to miss assignments at work. His kids noticed that he no longer spent time with them. They wondered what they had done wrong.

Frank himself wondered why he drank so much. He began treatment by considering what had been happening immediately prior to each spree. After considerable thought and discussion with his counselor, Frank noticed that there was a common thread underlying each outburst:

He had not gotten his way at work or at home. And when he did not get his way, he pouted. And then he drank. It looked like this:

Do not get my way ⟶ Pouting ⟶ Drinking

But this was not quite good enough for Frank because by the time he recognized that he was pouting, it was too late for him to stop himself from drinking. By then he was already in a bar. So he made an attempt to go a step further. He investigated his pouting in psychotherapy sessions.

Pouting for Frank turned out to be a substitute for an intense anger he felt. He was able to modify the sequence above to include the underlying emotion:

Do not get my way ⟶ Anger ⟶ Pouting ⟶ Drinking

Since it was too late to do anything about the sequence when he was pouting—it inevitably led to the bottle—Frank was now in a position to try to interrupt the progression to the bottle at an earlier step along the way. He could try to identify the warning signs of his emotional reaction.

Anger was associated with two warning signs for Frank. When he was angry, he learned, he was tense in several parts of his body, and his body shook. He had broken down the sequence still further into its basic components:

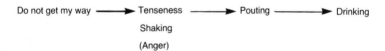

Do not get my way ⟶ Tenseness ⟶ Pouting ⟶ Drinking
　　　　　　　　　　　Shaking
　　　　　　　　　　　(Anger)

He was now able to work on finding alternatives to drinking as a way to cope with these signs of his troubles. He began to work on exercises to reduce the tension in his body and on relaxation exercises to help him calm down so that he could think about the source of his anger. And he began to consider ways to express his anger other than by drinking them away. He had, in effect, added to the diagram:

Situation	Warning Signs of Emotional Reaction	Alternatives to Resolve Tenseness and Shaking
Do not get my way	Tensenesss Shaking	Drinking Exercise Relaxation exercises Expression of anger

Now let's work on this example in terms of the chart below. (This is a simplified example for illustration purposes only. The steps for each of *your* emotions may be more difficult to arrive at.) Frank spent several weeks to get this far. But, for this one entry, Frank's chart looked like this:

	Step 1	Step 2	Step 3	Step 4	Step 5
What I gave up	Things that preceded my drinking	Emotions associated with Step 1	Warning signs	What alcohol did for me/ What I got from drinking	What else could do what the alcohol did?
Friendships Job Home Life Good Health	Do not get get my way	Anger	Tenseness Shaking	Calmed me down; helped me forget anger	Exercise; relaxation exercise; learn to express anger

To help you organize your thoughts and begin working on this five-step process for yourself, you can use the outline in Appendix C.

A Word about Your Thoughts

One ingredient is missing from the techniques we have just finished discussing. It concerns your thoughts. Frequently, various kinds of thoughts are involved in the process of deciding whether to drink in a particular circumstance. These thoughts can occur at several points. They might occur just before the point at which you are aware of an emotional reaction; that is, between Step 1 and Step 2. In the example above, when he didn't get his way, Frank explained to himself that "they are doing this to hurt me." Then he started to notice the warning signs of tenseness and shaking. At that point, between Steps 3 and 4, Frank recalled noting to himself, "What's going on? Things must be really out of control if I'm this tense and I'm shaking so. A drink is the only way I can cope with this." After his first drink, Frank recalls telling himself that "I've done it now. I'm going to be drinking all night."

At each point along the way, Frank concluded that he was doomed to pass to the next step in his drinking episode. Each thought, however, represented an *untested* conclusion. He had not examined it consciously, but it led him to take to actions consistent with the thought. In other words, Frank acted *as if* the conclusion about himself were true, without stopping to question if it were *indeed* true.

Thoughts you might have along the way in a drinking episode might concern conclusions like Frank made about his ability to cope or about the effects you expect from the alcohol you drink. They might, as well, concern other aspects of your life or relationships with others. The point here is that certain patterns of thinking, and certain specific thoughts of yours, can play important roles in the circumstances in which you drink—or start to drink again after stopping for a while. Those thoughts are early warning signs that the sequence you diagrammed for yourself in Appendix C might be underway. Learning to identify those thoughts early enough to take effective action could help you interrupt your drinking pattern, develop new ways to respond to those "high risk" circumstances, and lessen the chances of returning to old drinking patterns. Learning about them is best done with the help of a trained counselor.

SPECIALIZED TRAINING PROGRAMS

In addition to psychotherapy, alcoholism treatment often includes certain specialized training programs that help people do things in their lives in new ways—without alcohol.

We have been talking about discovering the role alcohol played in your life, what alcohol helped you do that you could not do in other ways. The trick to overcoming your dependence on alcohol rests in taking the next step, that of finding *other* ways to meet whatever needs alcohol met for you. Many treatment centers include specialized "skills training" programs that help people develop new ways to face life without alcohol. These programs aim to teach you how to master social skills in the areas of your life which have caused difficulty in the past.

Three skill programs in particular are often found in alcohol treatment programs. They are *Assertiveness Training*, *Drink Refusal Training*, and *Relaxation Training*.

Assertiveness Training

In general, Assertiveness Training aims to teach people how to communicate effectively. In particular, it helps people learn how to stand up for their own rights without infringing on the rights of others.

How does this relate to drinking problems? Many drinkers report difficulty in expressing themselves directly. They often think they need a couple of drinks before they can speak their minds. Unfortunately, often by the time they are ready to speak, the alcohol has taken over their minds.

Assertiveness Training sessions teach two important communication techniques. First, they train people to organize their thoughts so that they can speak simply and clearly. Their messages to other people are brief and to the point, and they avoid the pitfalls of unproductive communication. Second, they teach people that the *way* they say something is as important as *what* they say. People learn to pay conscious attention to their "body language," to such things as body posture, eye contact, hand gestures, facial expressions, and the inflection and volume of their voices. People learn that they need not have a drink in order to be able to speak their minds.

Drink Refusal Training

At first glance, the title of this type of training might seem ridiculous. "After all," you may say, "isn't all alcoholism treatment focused on helping people refuse drinking?"

To some degree, this is true. However, there are certain common situations in which drinkers encounter a great deal of pressure to drink—family celebrations, visits with old drinking buddies, business affairs. And it is truly surprising how difficult some people find it to refuse a drink, even when they do not want it.

For instance, as part of one inpatient alcoholism treatment program, a counselor periodically selects clients and constructs the following test. He and one client will meet in front of a group of clients. The counselor will say to the client, "Pretend you're home from the hospital for the weekend and I'm one of your old drinking buddies. I'm going to try to talk you into having a drink, and I want you to do everything you can to resist me." The client has a lot of advantages in this situation—the encouragement of the group, the knowledge that it is only "pretend," the need to impress the counselor with how well he is doing in treatment. Nevertheless, the counselor has seldom failed to talk the client into taking a drink. At the very least in this exercise, clients agree to accompany the counselor to a fictitious bar.

In many ways, Drink Refusal Training is similar to Assertiveness Training. However, some of the skills taught are specific to Drink Refusal Training. We will describe six of them here.

1. Make it clear to others, both verbally and nonverbally, that you are firm in your decision not to drink. As in Assertiveness Training, make sure your body language reinforces your words. Maintain eye contact with the other

person, stand up or sit up straight, and use forceful hand gestures.

2. Do not verbally attack the person who is trying to get you to drink. If you attempt to deal with his persistence by insulting or criticizing him, the focus of your talk with him will quickly change to a verbal battle about your criticism. That can be quite nerve-wracking, so stick to the point without bringing in personal criticisms or attacks. The point is that you have decided not to drink.

3. Make it as fast as possible. Do not prolong the talk about whether you will drink or not. Come to the point quickly. The more you talk about it, the greater the chances you will drink.

4. Try to be open to constructive compromise whenever possible. For example, if someone asks you to drink with him, maybe you could agree to go out for coffee instead. After all, by deciding to stop drinking alcohol, you have not necessarily decided to stop drinking *everything* with other people. Sometimes this compromise is an effective way to get others to stop encouraging you to drink alcohol. They may prefer to have your company while you drink a nonalcoholic beverage to not having your company at all.

5. Use humor if possible to break the tension with someone who is trying to get you to drink. A bit of humor may be enough to break the ice and help both of you become more comfortable, even though you are not drinking.

6. If other things do not work for you, try using a plausible reason for not drinking. Some people have found it useful to say they cannot drink alcoholic beverages because of illness or medications they are taking. Though some people consider this an undesirable alternative because it may not be fully true, it may be preferable to the consequences of feeling continued pressure to drink.

Relaxation Training

People often find it difficult to relax while in treatment. Many note that they have problems with "nerves" and that in the past alcohol has helped to calm them down. Relaxation Training is designed to teach people how to relax emotionally and physically without using alcohol or other drugs. It is based on a simple principle. People usually get nervous in their minds first. Soon, however, the nervousness is reflected in tension in their bodies. This tenseness, in turn, tends to make the mental nervousness worse, and so on in a vicious circle. Relaxation training consists of a series of exercises through which people can learn to interrupt this cycle.

Typically, Relaxation Training exercises teach several types of skills. Most training includes the progressive muscle relaxation technique, which consists of exercises in which people alternately tense and relax the various groups of muscles in their bodies, one at a time. By becoming aware of the feelings of relaxation by means of these exercises, a person can learn to recreate the feelings when he becomes tense in the future. It teaches a means of achieving a deeper state of muscle relaxation than usual. It was this technique that was particularly helpful for Linda.

The progressive muscle relaxation technique is often combined with other techniques of enhancing the ability to relax quickly. One such technique consists of associating a key word—perhaps "relax" or "calm"—with the relaxation exercises. This often results in a direct association between the key word and the relaxed state itself. It becomes possible, with practice, to use the key word directly to induce relaxation, even if the set of relaxation exercises is not completed.

A technique similar to the "key word" technique can be used. This technique uses things you can imagine in your mind's eye to help you relax. These images generally consist of relaxing scenes which people can bring to mind and concentrate on when they become tense. Typical scenes include laying on a beach, going for a walk through the woods, or floating on a rubber raft on a calm lake. You may find a different type of scene particularly helpful for you, but whatever the scene and whatever the technique that is most helpful for you, relaxation exercises are effective; it is difficult for the body to be tense if the mind can relax, and vice versa. If you can relax your mind with a peaceful image or scene, your body will have the chance to relax. And if you can find a way to relax your body, you are helping your mind calm down.

There may be other specialized treatment approaches in a particular treatment program. All these techniques are helpful in that they help you learn new ways to cope with problems related in drinking.

AS TREATMENT PROGRESSES

When we talked about our five-step model earlier, one important thing we stressed was how important it is for drinkers to become aware of which emotions precede their drinking. It is equally important for people to become aware of the emotions they experience as alcoholism treatment progresses and they begin to make improvements in their lives. The two we will discuss briefly here are among the most common emotions felt by people as their treatment progresses. They are optimism and fear, and they are important to know about because when they occur, they sometimes lead to overreactions.

Optimism

One way to think about treatment is that it helps people better understand themselves and the way they act and that it helps them develop the power to change things in their lives. One consequence of developing a sense of power over our lives is that it lets us feel good about ourselves and our lives, and it gives us a sense of optimism.

A sense of optimism is definitely a help to those who are venturing out to face the "real world" without alcohol. It may, however, sometimes make the world look *too* rosy. It is appropriate for a person to feel a lot better about himself when leaving an inpatient program than he did before entering the program. After all, the person made a decision to get help, a decision that has usually been postponed for some time. More important, the person *acted* on the decision—he got help. In addition, people usually feel much better physically after detoxification and a period of being "dry." And finally, a major financial burden has usually been lifted.

Sometimes, though, this feeling of optimism grows beyond reasonable proportions. In AA this feeling is referred to as "the pink cloud." In this stage, people can construct an unrealistically positive view of their lives—their spouses are saints, their children are angels, their bosses become great humanitarians who are concerned only with their recovery. While there might be a kernel of truth in each statement, life is seldom so simple as to be either all good or all bad.

It is not surprising that a "pink cloud" would occur for the newly sober. It is true that very good things accompany sobriety. People usually report physical improvements. They sleep better and their appetites have returned. They might find themselves with extra money. (One newly sober client was discouraged when a tire on his automobile was punctured. On going to the repair shop, he found he had saved so much "drinking money" in eight weeks that he was able to buy *four* new tires, not just the replacement.) Family and friends are often supportive, sometimes congratulatory.

However, on the other hand, it is worth noting that some newly sober people get a very distorted view of their lives. They might now deny other problems in their lives in much the same way that they previously denied their drinking problems. For example, one man whose wife had obtained an order of protection against his violence and had begun divorce proceedings created rather elaborate plans to return home to his "loving wife and family" after his discharge from the hospital. In other words, sometimes the "pink cloud" is an exaggeration of some positive events; other times it is a distortion of reality.

There is another factor that contributes to the "pink cloud," especially for people treated in inpatient programs —the urge to drink might not have returned yet. People in inpatient programs often note, "I've been here six weeks and I have no desire or craving for a drink." They forget that their time in the program is, in a way, a period in which they are separated and sheltered from the "real world." During this period they can work on developing the strength to face it once again. It is a time in which the "will" to stay sober has been strengthened. However, the "will" is often stronger than the "power" to stay sober.

Sometimes people are tempted to test their will after discharge from an inpatient program. They feel better, and they are very optimistic about their future sobriety—and, after all, why not be? They have come pretty far. "Why not buy a bottle or go to the old tavern?" you may find yourself asking. "I can do that. I don't *have* to drink." Or you might have a drink thinking that "*One* drink can't hurt." Many people are tempted to test their power to try to "prove" they've kicked the drinking problem. The problem is, though, that testing often catches a person unprepared, and soon he is right back where he was before treatment—drinking too much.

Fear

Oddly enough, some people never get a sense of optimism. For one reason or another they might be much more cautious about the future, even though they may be aware of the progress they have made in treatment. These people can be much more aware of their vulnerability, and they might worry about whether they will be successful in staying sober. While they were drinking, they got used to the idea that things do not go quite right for them. Now, after being involved in treatment, things usually have improved. "But surely," some think, "things are going *so* well now, that something bad is *bound* to happen."

This feeling may be particularly troubling if the alcohol treatment program has "repeaters" in it who are back for their second or third time around. One's optimism, confidence, and determination can be shaken by seeing others who have tried sobriety and failed. The "what-if" questions arise: "What if I'm like them? What if something happens to me? What if I don't make it? What if I can't make sobriety work for me?" These are common questions that many people ask about their future as treatment progresses.

And then there are the dreams some people have.

Dreams

Fred was an inpatient for two weeks when he had a disturbing dream. In his dream, he was in a store waiting to pay for the soft drinks he had come to pick up. Ahead of him in line was an old drinking buddy. After they exchanged greetings, the man asked him to go next door to a tavern for a drink. Fred initially refused, but he soon found himself walking out of the store and into the tavern. At that point, Fred woke up—scared.

He began to question his sincerity in the treatment program. "After all," he thought, "I came here determined to stop drinking and now I'm dreaming of drinking." He asked about the dream the next day in the psychotherapy session. From the discussion that followed, he learned that such dreams need not be so frightening.

Though they can be disturbing, "drinking dreams" can merely point up a conflict in each drinker that led him to treatment in the first place.

The conflict is that one part of the drinker wants to stop drinking—the part that brings him to treatment. But another part wants to keep on drinking. Our minds are quite selective in what they choose to remember. It is just like old Army buddies who laugh about the good times and forget all the bad ones. The same thing often happens with drinkers who swap *their* "war stories." All they remember is "the good times." In Fred's dream, for example, he might have remembered the music in the tavern, the laughing and joking there, or the cool comfort of the drink. But there were "bad times" that resulted from the drinking too— hangovers, family quarrels, physical illness. It is not unusual that your mind would gloss over the bad times of drinking. After all, drinking has been a part of your life —a way in which you have dealt with the world—for quite a while. Finding a new way to deal with the world is a difficult and even frightening task. When we encounter difficulties we often revert to our old ways of coping. So the temptation to drink will certainly recur.

When you think of the two parts of a drinker's psychological makeup, treatment of drinking problems tries to strengthen the part that wants to stop drinking so that it can overrule the part that wants to continue drinking. But while treatment can help overrule the second part, it does not eliminate that second part. What treatment does is to help you add the "power" to your "will" to stay sober.

Drinking dreams usually reflect the tension between the two parts of a person. They are not an ominous look into a mysterious unconscious; they are fairly accurate representations of what the person is beginning to come to terms with in treatment.

Optimism and fear are both experienced at one time or another by most people in treatment—so they are "normal." You can expect them. What is important is that they be seen in perspective. They need not be problems for you. In moderation, they are not harmful. If either feeling gets out of hand, it is a good idea to discuss it with someone who can help you figure out why it got out of hand. That someone can be a family member or friend, a staff member in a treatment program, or an AA member.

ADJUSTING TO SOBRIETY

The overall goal of treatment is to stop drinking altogether. However, there are the obstacles that a person must learn to overcome in order to reach that goal. These obstacles generally take longer to overcome than the two or three weeks the person may be in an inpatient rehabilitation program. People who complete an inpatient program are usually encouraged to continue treatment as outpatients in order to continue working on their problems—and with good reason. Studies have shown that people who continue in outpatient treatment are better able to maintain their sobriety, work on other personal problems, and put their lives back together than people who do not.

It is best to think of treatment as extending past the inpatient care you may start with. Outpatient care is the next logical step in treatment. But even if you enter outpatient treatment, there are some other things that you might encounter after discharge.

Physical Adjustment Problems

You may experience persistent physical adjustment problems. Some people find that it takes their bodies a while to get back into shape. Others experience problems sleeping or adjusting to a regular routine once again. Still others experience problems functioning sexually. People experience different problems—and some lucky souls experience none. You might need some professional help with the adjustment problems you may experience. Do not be afraid to seek that help, but also do not be too quick to throw in the towel if you have some physical problems. Be prepared to give yourself the time you need to adjust to sobriety.

"Dry Drunk"

Some newly sober people have an experience in which they might act as they characteristically do when drunk, even though they have not consumed any alcohol. They might find themselves to be irritable, argumentative, or tearful. There are several different ways of explaining this kind of experience. Some say it is due to the slow release of alcohol from the body. More likely, it occurs when a person stops drinking but does not learn new ways of coping with problems. As a result, his only outlet is the behavior he used when drunk.

Social and Psychological Problems

There are several social and psychological problems that commonly face people who have recently stopped drinking. The first of these concerns the change in the nature of relationships with others. A relationship is based on each partner playing a role. For example, in your drinking relationships, if you stop drinking, you also change your role as a "drinking buddy," and you can expect your relationships to change. Friendships based entirely on your drinking will probably end: your drinking partners will not be too interested in you (nor you in them) if you do not drink.

Relationships with friends, family, employers, and others can seem awkward at first when you are sober. For example, some people report great difficulty at holidays and family celebrations. When a toast is involved, your family might not know whether or not to fill your glass. If they do decide to fill the glass, they might debate what beverage to put in it. So even small details can lead to awkward situations.

In addition, the alcohol no longer interferes with how you relate to others. You will now be sober when you interact with them and therefore must relate to them in different ways. That was the problem Jerry and his family experienced after he stopped drinking.

A second difficulty facing some people is that they abruptly come face-to-face with the same problems they had before they sought treatment. Treatment can be a "shelter" from the real world. You may have decided during treatment to change your drinking behavior. Perhaps you also decided to change other behaviors so that you could deal with problems related to your drinking—and indeed, there they are waiting for you, all those things with which you were faced before you started your last drinking spree, just as you left them. If you had bills to pay, they are there. So are the problems you might have had with the house, the car, or the kids. So, too, are the other aggravations that bothered you before you came for treatment. You begin to deal differently with these problems while in treatment. Now you come face-to-face with the opportunity to put to work what you learned—and that can be difficult at first.

You might also find that people treat you differently. We have already talked about changes in your relationships with drinking buddies and with those close to you.

Some who know about your drinking problems and the treatment you had might be supportive and helpful. They will not offer you drinks, and they will encourage you to continue with appropriate treatment. They might even want to join you in that treatment. They will share in the excitement of your sobriety.

But others might not be so supportive. Some people might be suspicious or scornful of you and the efforts you make to deal with your drinking problems. They might not trust you now that you are sober any more than they did when you were drinking. They will reserve their judgments and wait to see if, at long last, *this* time you are going to make it.

In addition, there might be people who honestly liked you *better* when you were drinking. Some might be old drinking buddies who do not want you as a reminder of *their* excesses. Others might be superficial friends who like you better "jolly" and seemingly carefree. In some cases it can even be family members who like you better drinking.

For example, Timothy left an inpatient program with the strong support of his family. But it took only a week for his teenage daughters to become disenchanted with his sobriety. When he was drunk, they were able to borrow money from him freely. Now that he was sober, he was monitoring their spending habits more carefully. In addition, he was insisting that they clean their rooms before receiving *any* money. For them—at least in this respect—life was a lot easier when he drank!

Be prepared for this type of reaction from others. Think about how you would handle it. If you experience it, will it be enough to get you to drink again? You will probably be best off when you prepare yourself for the rude awakening that awaits you in the "real world" even after you have started to deal with your most visible problem—your drinking.

Such a rude awakening awaits many people who have been treated for drinking problems, whether in the hospital or as outpatients. Some of the potential surprises might have been softened as treatment progressed, but it is likely that a number of the problems you rediscover will persist for some time. They do not develop overnight, and they will not disappear overnight. Try to keep things in perspective. The goal of treatment is to help you begin the process of facing, dealing with, and resolving these problems. It is not to find the final solutions for all your problems. You will grow, learn, and change for the rest of your life. Use what is available to you to assist you in dealing with these problems. Treatment is one resource to help you change and adjust. Others are AA and—perhaps—Antabuse.

Money

A welcome benefit of sobriety that many drinkers do not realize concerns money. Many people discover to their surprise that they spent much more money on alcohol than they realized while they were drinking. Quite likely, a number of bills have piled up, and people have to face them once they are sober. But sometimes they also find that they have more money than they thought they would in order to put their lives back together. (Remember the man who went to buy a new tire?) For those people, the formerly impossible task of paying off the past and saving for the future suddenly becomes possible.

However, new-found money can be a mixed blessing. Saving money rightly suggests to people that they are once again in control of their lives. But for some people, an excess of money can be a cue for drinking. The experiences of one outpatient we know can be all too familiar. He stays sober and works until he is able to save $10,000. When he reaches this magic number he stops saving, starts drinking, and does not stop until he spends it all. Now he might not be a typical case, but he should remind you to ask yourself: "Will having more money cause me any problems?"

SLIPS

Now for a word about the unspeakable: A *slip* is a return to drinking during or after completion of treatment for a drinking problem. Those who treat people for drinking problems expect them to be tempted to drink after treatment, and they usually expect some people to slip. In fact, some research studies have suggested that slips are rather common. When a slip gets out of hand and a person starts drinking heavily again, it is referred to as a *relapse.*

Some of the signs of an impending slip can include the feeling of being "down in the dumps," the growing belief that your plans will not work, or the belief that your problems are too big to be resolved. Others are decreased patience with others, changes in your eating or sleeping patterns, increasing thoughts about drinking, and a general disappointment about your life. You might begin to feel that you are sliding inevitably toward the bottle. Some people report feeling happy and optimistic just before a slip. But whatever precedes it, the important thing about a "slip" is to be able to understand it.

A slip can be best understood within the context of the discussion we had earlier about psychotherapy. Just as it is important to understand what might contribute to your drinking, so too is it important to understand why you might slip after treatment. According to some researchers, approximately three out of four who suffer relapses do so (1) because they have difficulty dealing with frustration, anger, or other negative emotions; (2) because they have trouble dealing with conflicts they may have with others; or (3) because they cannot resist social pressures, including pressures others put on them to drink. It appears that only about one in 10 people who return to drinking does so because of some ill-defined "urge" or "taste" for a drink. And only one in 30 returns to drinking to recapture the pleasure of being "high" for its own sake. As you might suspect, the factors that contributed to their drinking in the first place ultimately are related for many people to their return to drinking. Slips can be understood.

Consider this case as an example: Barry had been drinking for 25 years, and his drinking had been a problem for 15 years when he first sought treatment. During his first inpatient rehabilitation program he learned about alcohol and its effect on his body. He also learned about the psychological, social, and family aspects of his drinking. After discharge, he began attending AA meetings regularly. He was treated in a second rehabilitation program approximately nine months after his first treatment had ended.

Following the treatment, Barry resumed his attendance at AA meetings. He also was faced again with conflict among members of his family, and again he reacted by beginning to drink. After about a week, he entered a detoxification program to dry out. From there he began attending outpatient treatment sessions at which he learned —among other things—to handle frustrating family situations and the anger he felt in a way other than by drinking. As outpatient treatment progressed, Barry was able to help resolve some of his family problems, and the frequency of family conflicts decreased.

In Barry's case, two circumstances were related to his drinking. One was that he encountered situations at home that made him angry and frustrated. The other was that Barry had adopted drinking as the way to handle the anger and frustration. Barry could do nothing to change the first circumstance—we all encounter unpleasant situations once in a while—but he did learn to change the second. He changed his reliance on alcohol as a way to handle family problems with his wife and children, and together they learned to work out problems that previously had been the causes of battles. Barry has made sure that the two circumstances that were so closely related to his drinking would not occur together again.

What can you do about a slip? It is important to be able to react appropriately to a slip. The first thing to recognize about a slip is that it is a serious matter. However, try to keep it in perspective if it happens to you. It is an *event*, not a glimpse into a declining future. A slip does not mean that you have failed or that you are doomed to a lifetime of alcoholism. It may simply be a sign of some unfinished business. Remember, you can do something about a slip. A quick return to treatment can often prevent a slip from becoming a tragedy. A slip can highlight a recurrent problem area, and it allows you to pick up where you left off working on the problem. It can be handled much as we have discussed handling drinking problems in general. Working on whatever contributed to the slip can help you finish the unfinished business from your previous treatment. It might also increase your chances of mastering your drinking problem in the future. If there is one thing we stress in our work with drinkers, it is that they can regain control over their lives and stop drinking—even if, at first, they do not believe they can. It is in this respect that we have suggested some very specific steps you can take to start working on your drinking problem.

Chapter 4

Alcoholics Anonymous

For many people, "alcoholism treatment" and "Alcoholics Anonymous" are synonymous. There are several reasons for this confusion. First, AA has been in existence longer than most other forms of alcoholism treatment. The program's formal origins date back to 1938, although the founders first met in 1935. Second, AA is by far the most widespread form of treatment. As of 1975 there were formal registered AA groups in 95 countries. The 1985 AA census estimated that there were over 1.5 million members worldwide, with more than 800,000 of them in the United States and Canada. One indication of the magnitude of AA's size is that over 34,000 people attended its 1985 annual convention.

Even though AA and alcoholism treatment are not truly synonymous, AA remains a major form of treatment, if only because of its longevity and its size. But the primary reason AA is a major form of treatment for those with drinking problems is that a great many people over the years have found AA to be extremely helpful. Some in AA have found it to be the *only* effective form of treatment for them. Other AA members combine participation in AA with the other forms of treatment we have described in this book.

In this chapter we will introduce you to the AA program. First we will present a brief description of the AA program and its various components: meetings, publications, and sponsors. Then we will attempt to give some overall perspective with regard to AA and alcoholism treatment in general. We will list various AA publications that will help you gain a more comprehensive view of the program. We encourage you to complete our introduction to AA by attending an AA meeting. Then decide if AA is for you.

PROGRAM DESCRIPTION

Earlier in this book we said it is difficult to say what the typical problem drinker is like because drinkers come in so many varieties. The AA program mirrors the population of problem drinkers in its diversity. It is hard to make general statements about AA because it is a very flexible organization. There is a bureaucratic structure that handles functions such as the distribution of publications, but its affairs are not important to our discussion of AA as a form of treatment.

The general guidelines under which AA operates as an organization are known as the Twelve Steps and Twelve Traditions. Nevertheless, the AA program is adapted to meet the needs of the members in each group. The major components of the AA program, however, remain the same across groups—the meetings, the literature, the Twelve Steps, and sponsors.

ENTERING THE PROGRAM

Joining AA is very simple. In its own words, "the only requirement for membership is a desire to stop drinking." The way you join AA is to attend meetings. Period. There are no formal membership criteria, application procedures, referral forms, or review boards, and there is no fee structure.

MEETINGS

Many of us have a notion of AA meetings as huge affairs with formal agendas and rigid formats. Actually, though, AA meetings are quite flexible in both content and format. There are some distinctions in AA meetings that are worth noting.

Beginners' meetings are usually much smaller than general AA meetings. Beginners' meetings occur either prior to a general meeting, or as a subsection of a general meeting. In these meetings, experienced AA members describe the program to new members and answer any questions they might have. "Beginners" are usually considered to be those who have attended fewer than six AA meetings.

Open and Closed Meetings

In schedules of AA meetings, programs are designated as "open" or "closed." It is worth knowing the difference.

Anyone may attend an *open* AA meeting, whether he thinks he has an alcohol problem or not. A typical format for open meetings is that two or three members present their stories. While there is no rigid format for their presentations, they usually discuss their early use of alcohol, how alcohol came to interfere with their lives, their introduction to the AA program, and the positive steps they have taken since joining AA. Open meetings are quite useful to a new AA member in helping him find people with whom he can identify. They are helpful to older members because such meetings help prevent them from becoming complacent. One AA publication sums it up this way: " . . . the reminders you get of the miseries of active alcoholism can help extinguish any lurking desire to take a drink."

Closed meetings are restricted to those who think they have a drinking problem. While one member might open the meeting by telling his story, closed meetings are usually discussion meetings. Sometimes the meeting focuses on a particular topic, such as "trust" or "humility." But very often a member of the group will share some recent triumph or tragedy. Other members then help provide support and relate how similar experiences have affected them. The primary focus of these discussions is sobriety, and many helpful techniques are shared.

It should be noted that a steady diet of only one kind of meeting—open or closed—is usually not beneficial. Participation in only open meetings, for example, can enable the drinker to remain somewhat uninvolved. In particular, it does not provide a format for examining one's sobriety and discussing new coping strategies. Attendance at only closed meetings, on the other hand, helps the drinker look at his drinking behavior through rose-colored glasses. How convenient it is for all of us to forget our past mistakes. Many drinkers say, "What do I want to listen to that guy for? I did all those things myself." Precisely—and, as the AA slogan says, "Remember when."

Step Meetings

As in the closed "topic" meetings, some AA meetings devote themselves to discussion of one or more of the Twelve Steps. Some people's reaction is, "Why do I need a meeting to discuss the Steps? I've read them already."

The steps are like the Ten Commandments—the rules themselves are simple enough; it is the number of situations in which they can be applied that requires explanation. Since the Twelve Steps are the core of the AA program, any means by which a member can understand them better is valuable.

LITERATURE

There are several reasons why reading AA literature is beneficial to the AA member. First, it can help provide a deeper understanding of the program than is available from meetings. Second, there is a wide variety of literature and at least part of each publication addresses some special interest group. Third, the literature can be carried easily enough by the member and can be reviewed in a crisis.

Deeper Understanding

Some members refer to AA literature as "a meeting in print," and this seems an apt description. Take one example: The concept of a "Higher Power" is central to successful participation in AA. Yet it is often a difficult concept to grasp. None of the members at a particular AA chapter might have an interpretation of the Higher Power which makes sense to an individual member. One pamphlet contains 75 interpretations of the concept from various members. The variety of viewpoints represented makes it unlikely that a member could not find one to his liking.

Variety

AA World Services, Inc., prints a selection of books about alcoholism and AA. We want to describe a few of them here. Probably the best-known book is *Alcoholics Anonymous*, also known as the "Big Book." While a number of early members contributed to the book, the first portion of it was written by Bill W., a co-founder of AA. The basic precepts of AA are presented in this book, and it is regarded as the primary sourcebook by most AA members. The book was AA's first publication.

A more recent publication is *Living Sober*, which is subtitled "Some methods AA members have used for not drinking." This relatively short book (87 pages) lives up to its subtitle. The book is informally written and focuses primarily on practical tips on how to stay sober. It is not the kind of book to read in one sitting. Its best use is similar to that of Dr. Spock's *Baby and Child Care*—i.e., as a resource book for solutions to particular problems.

Another book that is best digested piecemeal is *Twenty-Four Hours a Day*. In this book, each page is devoted to a different day of the year, and a short essay appears on each page. The topics vary, but the tone is generally inspirational. Some AA members report that they start their day by reading the appropriate page from this book. By doing so, they begin the day with a positive mental attitude that is not easily disturbed by the events of the day. (*Twenty-*

Four Hours a Day is not an "official" AA publication, but its presence throughout AA is nearly universal.)

AA also prints a number of pamphlets. Some of these address particular subgroups (the military, industry, young people, women, drug abusers) while others concern more general issues. Excellent introductory works include *This is AA, Is AA For You?*, and *The Jack Alexander Article.* These pamphlets can help the prospective member learn what to expect from AA meetings.

Portability and Use in a Crisis

As we said, AA literature is sometimes referred to as "a meeting in print." There are times when an AA member cannot attend a meeting just when it is needed most, perhaps during a physical illness or while at work. The use of AA literature can be most useful during those critical times that are most likely to lead to a relapse.

Some of the most helpful publications for such times are those which contain either the Serenity Prayer or some of the AA slogans. The Serenity Prayer states "God grant me the serenity to accept the things I cannot change, the courage to change the things I can, and the wisdom to know the difference." While this prayer did not originate with AA, it has become well adapted to its members' uses. Many drinkers have reported that a recitation of this prayer has given them the moment's pause they needed to re-evaluate a situation before returning to drinking.

In AA, the saying "Remember When" is called a slogan. Other AA slogans are Easy Does It; Just for Today; Live and Let Live; First Things First. As with the Serenity Prayer, some of these sayings have been around for years and certainly did not originate with AA. However, as used by AA, they represent a shorthand version of various aspects of the AA program.

THE STEPS

The core of the AA program itself is the Twelve Steps. All meetings revolve around the Twelve Steps and all writings are based on the Twelve Steps. These are the Twelve Steps, as devised by the early members of AA:

1. We admitted we were powerless over alcohol—that our lives had become unmanageable.
2. Came to believe that a power greater than ourselves could restore us to sanity.
3. Made a decision to turn our will and our lives over to the care of God *as we understood Him.*
4. Made a searching and fearless moral inventory of ourselves.
5. Admitted to God, to ourselves, and to another human being the exact nature of our wrongs.
6. Were entirely ready to have God remove all these defects of character.
7. Humbly asked Him to remove our shortcomings.
8. Made a list of all persons we had harmed, and became willing to make amends to them all.
9. Made direct amends to such people wherever possible, except when to do so would injure them or others.
10. Continued to take personal inventory, and when we were wrong, promptly admitted it.
11. Sought through prayer and meditation to improve our conscious contact with God *as we understood Him,* praying only for knowledge of His will for us and the power to carry that out.
12. Having had a spiritual awakening as the result of these steps, we tried to carry this message to alcoholics, and to practice these principles in all our affairs.

While there are many ways to analyze the Steps, they seem to represent four stages of the recovery process—surrender, assessment, making amends, and carrying the message.

Surrender

The first three Steps involve "the surrender process." In this process, the drinker comes to realize that he is not able to moderate his drinking. This process is not easy for most drinkers. Many relapses result when the drinker thinks, "I've been sober six months now. I can handle just one or two drinks." In the AA framework, this kind of thinking serves as evidence that this person has not yet "taken the First Step," that he does not yet see himself as truly "powerless" over alcohol.

The other part of the surrender process is that the new member accepts that there is a "Power greater than ourselves" and that he asks that Power for help. This step is often difficult for the new AA member. Many new members are not actively religious and do not believe in a "God." What is often helpful at this stage is to emphasize that even if the drinker cannot yet deeply believe in a "Power," at least he can recognize that he has not managed his life well up to this point. As a result, he should give up his often powerful need for control and instead be open to the advice of others. Some members find that after some successful participation in AA, they come to see the spirit of fellowship in AA as their "Higher Power." In other words, they believe that with the help of other members they can accomplish feats that previously had exceeded their grasp.

Assessment

The Fourth through Seventh Steps involve making an honest assessment of one's flaws, sharing the results of this assessment with another person, letting the Higher Power remove these character defects, and asking Him to do so.

Many people who relapse despite participation in AA have ignored, from the program's perspective, one or more components of the assessment sequence.

Honest assessment. Just by participating in AA meetings, one is admitting to problems with alcohol. And most of us are willing to admit to superficial flaws. However, the key word in the Fourth Step is *fearless*. In a fearless moral inventory we probe all those areas that we do not ever let ourselves think about—for example, that we have failed our children, ruined our health, or destroyed our marriage. These assessments seem to have more impact if they are done in writing. The Hazelden Corporation has published two excellent pamphlets that serve as guides to completing the assessment necessary to success in AA. (Hazelden's address is in the Resources chapter.)

Sharing the assessment. If the assessment is done well, there will undoubtedly be a lot of painful memories brought to light. During the assessment, the member cannot help but become aware of certain weaknesses or flaws in himself. AA calls these flaws "character defects," and the process of exploring them is called "taking inventory." Some of these character defects might seem so shameful or embarrassing that the member cannot picture ever sharing that material with anyone. But through participation in AA, the material is often gradually revealed. As other AA members share their stories, the new member can identify with various aspects and therefore share his material. After a certain amount of time in AA, most members find someone with whom they feel particularly comfortable and to whom they reveal the rest of their inventory. This sharing need not be done with an AA member, merely with "another human being." Ministers, counselors, close friends, and relatives have all been used in this sharing process.

Be willing to be changed. The Sixth and Seventh Steps of AA are sometimes difficult ones for drinkers who do not have a sense of a spiritual God. There are at least three points that can be helpful in this process. First, once a drinker has honestly looked at his flaws and discussed them with someone else, he is usually ready—even eager—to have them removed. And so he asks God, Lady Luck, Fate, or whatever sense of Higher Power he has to help him by removing these flaws. This procedure does not imply that he does not need to work hard on improving himself, but merely that he leaves himself open for assistance.

Second, the key word in Step Seven may well be *humbly*. It is hard not to let your pride get in the way when asking for help with your flaws. The pride can show itself as "I did lie to my family a lot, but at least I never abused them physically." Drinkers are reluctant to admit that they are not in complete charge of their behavior when drinking. As a result, they congratulate themselves for whatever control they *did* have—they never spent the *whole* paycheck on booze, or cheated on their spouses, or used narcotics.

But another kind of pride is the false pride some drinkers take in just how bad they really were—"I was the worst. My bartender says he never saw anyone drink so much." At first this kind of statement seems to be the exact opposite of the kind discussed previously. After all, this kind of drinker is admitting how *bad* he was, not covering it up. But the important point to remember is that in each case the drinker is presenting himself as someone special, someone so unique that any general rules do not apply to him. He is either so controlled in his drinking that he does not need to stop, or so uncontrolled that he cannot be *expected* to stop. The Sixth and Seventh Steps of AA help the drinker see himself in proper perspective and ask for help.

Making Amends

During the assessment process, the drinker often comes to recognize the ways in which he has hurt others. The Eighth and Ninth Steps involve recognizing that you have hurt others and are beginning to make amends to them. As an AA pamphlet notes, these steps can be quite satisfying in that they involve concrete action. There are often a number of tangible amends that need to be made—financial debts to be repaid, "borrowed" belongings to be returned, damaged property to be restored, and long-neglected chores to be completed. In addition, there are usually a lot of apologies owed to others—employers, neighbors, friends, relatives, spouses, and children. The apologies need not be overly flowery or excessively humble; an admission of past wrongs, expression of regret, and promise of future change is all that is required for most. In some cases the people may be so annoyed with the drinker that the apology is better done by letter than in person. It is also important to remember the second half of the Ninth Step, that drinkers should make amends " . . . except when to do so would injure them or others." For example, you may have pilfered money from your daughter's piggy bank, but have already replaced it without her knowledge. If she truly does not already know this, the information might be best kept to yourself.

"Carrying the Message"

In Steps Ten and Eleven, AA members work to consolidate the gains made in previous steps. In Step Twelve, they venture out to help those earlier along in their attempts to stop drinking.

The practice of the Twelfth Step is central to both the positive and negative stereotypes of AA. In the positive stereotype, selfless AA members will appear any time of the day or night to provide any form of help to a "drunk." In the negative stereotype, AA fanatics go about preaching the AA "gospel," badgering those with no significant drinking problems. As with all stereotypes, both are inaccurate.

AA emphasizes that much of the spirituality in its program can be defined as "love." Many new members report being impressed with how much the members genuinely care for each other, with no thought of repayment. The experience of such a spirit of genuine caring can certainly be referred to as a spiritual experience, and it is this message that AA wants its members to carry to others: There is help available from people who genuinely care. The literature emphasizes that this message should be carried willingly and unselfishly. In particular, those doing "Twelfth Step work" should not expect any additional reward if their message is effective, nor let their lives be disrupted if the message is rejected.

Twelfth Step work is only done with those who request it and is not forced on anyone. All type of aid will be offered to help the person get sober. However, this help need not include, for example, becoming a taxi service or bodyguard. Only the help that will aid someone in beginning a program of sobriety need be offered.

The negative stereotype has some kernels of truth. Some members who do Twelfth Step work are quite dogmatic and insistent. They may seem like fanatics. However, every collection of human beings has a certain percentage of fanatics, and AA undoubtedly has its share. Some "fanatics" may be new members of AA. Like all people who have found something new they enjoy, their enthusiasm may override their common sense. However, these people are in the minority in AA. And since Twelfth Step work is done in pairs, it is highly unlikely that both members would be equally dogmatic. One usually balances the other.

Having described the Twelve Steps, the most important thing to emphasize is that they constitute a circular —not a linear—process. In other words, the Twelve Steps are not like a recipe for sobriety that you start at Step One, go through to Step Twelve and then expect sobriety to bloom. Instead, it is a process of continuing reappraisal and growth. For example, in doing Twelfth Step work, you can discover things about yourself that you did not know when you initially passed through the Fourth Step. Thus, none of the Steps is ever irrevocably "completed."

Finally, it is worth noting that not all AA members go through the Steps in order. Some prefer to begin making amends before they have completed their assessment. The important thing is not to ignore any of the Steps totally. True, there are sober people in AA who have not yet taken the Fifth Step. But since they have not, they are not really receiving the full benefit of the program.

SPONSORS

Another important aspect of the AA program is the sponsor relationship. A sponsor is an experienced AA member who becomes the new member's teacher, guide, "Big Brother," mentor. It is a relationship in which the sponsor has a varying degree of responsibility for the member. At the very least, the sponsor is supposed to guide the participation of the new member, offering helpful pamphlets, describing good meetings, introducing him to other members who might be helpful. The sponsor might also help arrange transportation to and from meetings if necessary. Sponsors usually confer with new members to help assess their progress in the program. The conferences may be at the member's house, by telephone, or over coffee after a meeting.

At the next level of responsibility, the sponsor is a major resource for the member in crisis. It is the sponsor who is called by a member if he becomes jittery at night, or feels the urge to drink. As warranted, the sponsor can invite the member to his house or travel to the member's home.

Finally, a sponsor helps a member get professional assistance, as necessary, should he suffer a relapse. The sponsor also assumes responsibility for seeing that a hospitalized member has visitors.

The sponsor relationship is definitely an important part of the AA program, but it is also an aspect that can be easily abused. Some members choose sponsors too quickly because of their excessive dependency needs, others because they think they "must" have a sponsor in order to be full-fledged AA members. No matter what the reason, a good degree of care should be exercised in the selection of a sponsor. As one AA member has said, "Choosing a sponsor is like buying shoes—choose what you can be comfortable with over a long period of time."

The other problem with sponsorship is not so much its abuse as its neglect. Some members participate in meetings and follow the program fairly well without ever choosing a sponsor. While sponsorship is not mandatory for AA membership, it is a helpful tool. Should a new member believe he does not need a sponsor, he should probably give it some more thought. It is hard to believe that a member has attended various meetings of AA for a period of time and has not found anyone whose advice he values and who therefore would be a good sponsor.

In addition, remember that once you find a sponsor, you need not keep that same sponsor forever. Some sponsors are better for particular stages of sobriety—the very active sponsor may be best for the initial stages of sobriety, a less directive one later on. Also, since both the sponsor and the member are improving and growing, they may grow away from each other. Traits they shared or enjoyed in each other at first may change over time. If any of these conditions occurs, there is no reason not to replace the sponsor or even to have two sponsors. One caution is that sometimes one is tempted to replace a sponsor because he is telling you what you may need—but may not *want*—to hear. AA will encourage you not to replace a sponsor casually.

AA IN PERSPECTIVE

As we said at the beginning of the chapter, some people equate Alcoholics Anonymous with the treatment of alcoholism. There are, of course, many other forms of treatment.

There are some who say that no one can get sober without AA. If someone seems to get better without AA, then one of two tautological responses is often given: Either he wasn't *really* addicted to alcohol in the first place, or he is not really sober but just on a "dry drunk."

Naturally, this whole line of reasoning is ridiculous. There are numerous examples of people who stopped drinking and adopted a sober lifestyle without the use of AA or any other form of treatment. Some become sober through a religious experience; others for a variety of other reasons.

What *can* be said is that participation in AA makes it much easier for some people to stop drinking and stay sober. For many people, participation in AA makes a resumption of drinking less likely.

Becoming Involved in AA

There are a number of steps one can take to become involved in AA. The first step would be to approach AA with the positive proper attitude. It helps to remind yourself that there are many advantages to the AA program.

1. *AA is well-established.* As we noted earlier, AA has been around for more than 50 years and has helped many thousands of people in that time. So you will not be dealing

with some crackpot organization, the newest fad to come along.

2. *AA is free.* Drinking is an expensive hobby. It becomes doubly expensive if it has led to unemployment, disability, alimony, or attorney's fees for a DUI charge. There is no charge for AA's help.

3. *AA's help is immediate.* When you want help from a hospital, clinic, or social service agency, sometimes you have to wait. At best, you must wait while you make application and your application is reviewed. At worst, you are put on a waiting list until an appointment can be arranged. In AA, you get help by going to a meeting.

4. *AA's help is widely available.* There are almost 20,000 AA groups in the United States. There are also AA meetings throughout the world. In urban areas people have a number of meetings available and can choose the ones best suited to them. In rural areas, AA meetings may not be as numerous, but they are often more accessible than treatment centers.

5. *AA members are supportive.* They are a group of people who are happy that you are not drinking. People who stop drinking, like those who stop smoking or lose weight, report some disappointment when people do not share their excitement at their accomplishment. "Is that all there is?" "Where's the parade?" In AA, you will find a group of people who are excited that you have stopped drinking. They may even celebrate "anniversaries" of your last drink at three months, six months, one year, and yearly thereafter.

It is important to have this kind of support because not everyone will necessarily be happy that you have stopped drinking. Your old drinking buddies, for instance, might not mind your "going on the wagon" but may see your stopping as a threat to their own well-being. Rather than being happy for your accomplishment, they might encourage you to resume drinking.

6. *AA meetings give you a chance to socialize.* Many people report that they drink in order to socialize. They like stopping at the tavern to see old friends, talk about

sports or politics, and unwind. AA meetings can give you the same chance to socialize, but without drinking. As one person put it, "I even saw some of my old drinking buddies at AA meetings. The only difference was that none of us was drunk."

It is not unusual for members to go out for coffee after an AA meeting. There are also AA-sponsored social events such as picnics and Christmas and New Year's Eve parties. So when you stop drinking by attending AA, you haven't lost your drinking friends as much as you have exchanged them for new *non*-drinking friends.

7. *AA offers you anonymity.* You need never even identify yourself by name if you do not want to. While the stigma of a drinking problem may not be as severe as it once was, some people prefer to maintain their privacy as they seek help for their drinking problem.

Beginning Attendance

The easiest way to attend AA meetings, like any other new activity, is to go with someone. In this case it is often best to attend your first few meetings with someone who is familiar with the program. You might have a relative, neighbor, or a co-worker who attends AA. In most cases they would be happy to accompany you to a meeting. You need not feel reluctant to ask their assistance, even if you have refused their help in the past. There are very few AA members who took help when it was first made available to them.

But let us suppose that you are not aware of anyone who attends AA. If you wish, you can call the local AA number and arrange to have a member greet you at the meeting place and introduce you to other members.

Naturally, you are free to attend meetings by yourself. However, sometimes unaccompanied new members isolate themselves and tend not to become very involved in the meetings.

People often ask, "How long should I attend AA and how frequently should I go?" The answer is, of course, that you should go as often and as long as you think you need to. While there are no regulations regarding attendance, we have found that there are some minimum guidelines. One rule of thumb is that you should attend at least six meetings before you decide whether to continue. In attending meetings, make sure you include a mix of open and closed meetings.

In terms of how often to attend AA, consider attending at least two meetings weekly. Since all human beings have a tendency to backslide, when you backslide from two meetings you might at least be attending one meeting a week. If you only attend meetings once weekly, it is much easier to backslide to none.

In the early stages of participation in AA, it is helpful to attend many different meetings to find the group in which you feel the most comfortable. Nevertheless, it is helpful to pick one group that you will attend weekly and make it your "home group." With regular attendance you can form deeper relationships with the other members. It is also one of the best ways to select a sponsor.

Family members and friends are welcome to attend open AA meetings. In some cases it has proved to be the first thing the drinker and his spouse have done together in a long time. Joint attendance is particularly useful for the drinker who becomes extremely active in AA. Sometimes family and friends can feel left out. Some spouses say, "So what if he stopped drinking! He used to spend all his time in a bar; now he spends all of it at AA meetings. *I* still never see him." Attending AA meetings together can be one way to mend these damaged relationships.

There are two pieces of AA literature that are especially helpful for the new member. The first is a schedule of the local meetings. It is easier to attend meetings if you have your own list of when and where they meet.

The second is the primary piece of AA literature, the book *Alcoholics Anonymous*, also known as the "Big Book." If you do not have the funds to purchase a copy, there are usually copies available at the local library. Other members might lend you a copy if you ask them.

In summary, we are not saying AA is the only way to stop drinking. Clearly it is not. And we are not saying that you cannot stop drinking if you do not attend AA, because you can. What we *are* saying is that AA is an extremely useful tool that you can use in a variety of ways to help you stop drinking. Hundreds of thousands of people have used it successfully over the years. We encourage you to try it as well.

Chapter 5

Antabuse: The Willpower Pill

In alcoholism treatment, Antabuse is often known as "The Pill." Like the *other* pill, Antabuse is taken to prevent slips. *Unlike* the other pill, however, it is taken by both men and women. Although it is a form of medication that has been in use for over 30 years, Antabuse is not widely known by the general public. In fact, it is often only those associated with the treatment of alcoholism (the drinker, his family, physician, attorney, probation officer, etc.) who are familiar with it. Even among those familiar with it, Antabuse has spawned a number of myths about its effects and side effects.

The use of Antabuse in the treatment of alcoholism has an interesting history. Thiram, a chemical component similar to Antabuse, was used for many years in the rubber industry. It was apparent that workers exposed to thiram became quite ill when they drank alcohol. At about the same time, in 1947, two Danish physicians working on the treatment of worms tested various promising compounds. They both took portions of one of these compounds, which was later given the generic name *disulfiram* and the trade name Antabuse. At a party shortly after taking the drug, they both experienced unpleasant reactions after a drink or two. They tested disulfiram further and discovered that it produced strong reactions in drinking volunteers.

These reactions, they reasoned, might deter people from drinking and, after further testing, Antabuse was introduced in 1948 as a treatment for chronic alcoholism.

Initial reaction was that Antabuse would be the miraculous cure for alcoholism. In the early 1950s it was used enthusiastically by physicians, but it soon became apparent that there were several significant problems with its use.

First, in the early days Antabuse was often prescribed in extremely high doses. In dosages above 500 milligrams per day, Antabuse may have several unpleasant side effects—fatigue or headache, for example—even if a person does not drink. If he does, the Antabuse reaction is itself proportionately stronger. Second, the types of people for whom Antabuse was dangerous were not well-known at that time, and it was prescribed for some people whose health made them marginal candidates. As a result, some very serious reactions were reported after some early patients drank alcohol while taking Antabuse. In fact, some Antabuse reactions proved fatal.

A third problem with the early use of Antabuse concerned what was called the "test dose," or "Antabuse challenge." The challenge consisted of giving a small amount of alcohol to a patient after he had been taking Antabuse for several days, thus producing an Antabuse reaction. This was done for two reasons. Initially, physicians wanted their patients to realize that Antabuse was a powerful medication and not just a sugar tablet or placebo. By experiencing a mild Antabuse reaction in a controlled setting, patients could learn to appreciate fully the seriousness with which they would have to treat Antabuse. But there was often an unspoken hope that experiencing a reaction would create enough fear in patients that they would be unlikely to try to sneak a drink on their own. There was even some hope that the whole Antabuse challenge would be so unpleasant that the taste of alcohol itself would become equally unpleasant to the drinker.

In the 1960s, Antabuse began to fall from favor as a treatment for alcoholism. Physicians were reluctant to subject their patients to what sometimes seemed to be the punishment of an Antabuse challenge. In addition, drinkers themselves resisted the challenge. The news of severe and fatal reactions spread quickly through the medical community and to those drinkers who might be appropriate candidates for Antabuse treatment. Antabuse came to be regarded as a drug too dangerous to use in any but the most extreme cases.

There were, however, several physicians who continued to explore the use of Antabuse. Dr. Ruth Fox was among the first to reduce the daily dose of Antabuse to an initial 500 milligrams from what was then the customary dose of 2000 milligrams. She also reduced the initial 500 milligram dose to 250 milligrams as a maintenance dose after the first days of treatment. These reduced doses were effective in treatment—combined with alcohol, they still produced the unpleasant reaction—yet they largely eliminated the unpleasant side effects of taking the drug.

The use of Antabuse as one part of treatment in alcoholism treatment programs grew in the 1970s. It is now common for alcohol treatment programs at least to have Antabuse available for use by their patients.

ANTABUSE SIDE EFFECTS

Even with the reduced dosage, Antabuse can have some minor side effects. The most common complaints include drowsiness, skin rash, headaches, a metallic aftertaste, and impotence. Not everyone experiences these symptoms, and even for those who do, the side effects either disappear over time by themselves or after the dose of the drug is reduced somewhat.

In some cases it is hard to know whether the side effects some people experience are due to the Antabuse or to the alcohol abuse that the Antabuse is helping to treat. Take drowsiness, for example: As noted in Chapter 1, chronic abuse of alcohol can lead to sleep problems. Can we tell, then, whether a person's drowsiness is due to the Antabuse he is taking or to the body adjusting itself to functioning without alcohol? Usually not, but in either case, the solution is relatively easy: Antabuse can be taken at bedtime. If the drug is causing drowsiness, there is no better time for it to do so.

The skin rash that can result from Antabuse usually looks like a mild form of acne. If the rash continues over time, it often disappears if the dosage of Antabuse is reduced. The same is true for both the headaches and the aftertaste. The headaches are usually mild, and the aftertaste is not so much harsh as strange. People describe it as garlic-like or metallic, and it generally fades over time. Once again, these problems respond well to reduction in dose.

Drowsiness, skin rash, and headaches are mild in nature and usually not too objectionable to most patients. The last side effect, impotence, usually is objectionable. Fortunately, it is not a frequent side effect. Like drowsiness, it is difficult to determine whether impotence is due to Antabuse or to alcohol abuse; like sleep problems, it is a relatively common result of chronic heavy drinking. For those people who continue to experience impotence, physicians may stop the use of Antabuse for some time. If the problem then does not disappear, the impotence most likely resulted either from the patient's heavy drinking or from psychological problems.

THE ANTABUSE REACTION

The mild unpleasantness of the side effects are minor compared to the experience of an Antabuse reaction. What does an Antabuse reaction feel like? Even those people who have had *mild* Antabuse reactions report them as being *very* unpleasant. These people often say, "I thought I was going to die." Ask Donald.

Donald was a young, husky man who often got into fights when he got drunk. He had spent time in jail for assault after one of his drunken bar fights. Since he never got into fights while sober, his attorney suggested he get treatment for his drinking problem. Donald cooperated

The Four Degrees of Antabuse Reactions

Degree	Symptoms
Mild	Flushing; headache; feeling of choking; head and neck throbbing.
Moderate	Sweating; thirst; chest pain; difficulty breathing; nausea; vomiting.
Severe	Heart pounding; dizziness; weakness; rapid breathing; blood pressure drop.
Fatal	Unconsciousness; seizures; heart failure; death.

well with the treatment program and even asked to take Antabuse.

Two weeks after he started treatment, Donald's fiancee visited him and told him that their engagement was off, whether or not he quit drinking. Donald was furious, and he stormed out of the hospital. It was a hot summer day, and as he passed by a tavern, he thought, "Boy, could I use a cold beer." He went into the tavern, ordered a beer, and drank it down. Nothing happened. "I *knew* all that stuff they said about Antabuse was a crock," he later recalled saying to himself.

He left the tavern and resumed walking. About a half-mile down the street, Donald noticed he was even hotter than before. So he bought a quart of beer at a delicatessen and drank it as he continued to walk down the street. He began to feel queasy, had a bad headache, and was sweating a lot. Suddenly it was hard for him to breathe. As he stopped to catch his breath, Donald suddenly felt like he was "having a heart attack." He was dizzy, he could not breathe and "I thought my heart was going to pound out of my chest." The next thing he remembered was being lifted from the sidewalk into an ambulance by the Rescue Squad.

He was taken to the emergency room of a nearby hospital and admitted to the Intensive Care Unit.

There are probably a lot of questions that come to mind: Why did he get such a bad reaction? Are all reactions that bad? Why didn't he know something was wrong immediately? Can some people who take Antabuse drink safely?

First, let's explain why combining alcohol with Antabuse leads to an unpleasant physical reaction. As you remember from Chapter 1, the liver metabolizes alcohol into carbon dioxide and water. At an intermediate state in that process, alcohol is changed into a chemical called *acetaldehyde*, which can have toxic effects when it accumulates in the body.

Usually, acetaldehyde is metabolized rather quickly into acetic acid (vinegar), which the body excretes. But Antabuse blocks the breakdown of acetaldehyde and allows it to accumulate in the blood. The acetaldehyde interacts with other chemicals in the body to lead to a decrease in blood pressure and to other symptoms that the drinker soon feels.

Donald's reaction was quite dramatic, and in a moment we will talk about why it was so bad. But first it is worth knowing that there are different degrees, or stages, of Antabuse reactions.

The severity of an Antabuse reaction depends mainly on three things: the amount of Antabuse in a person's body, the amount of alcohol consumed, and the person's physical condition.

Amount of Antabuse

We have already mentioned dosages of Antabuse and that it is now prescribed in lower doses than it used to be. But Antabuse can last in the body for up to 14 days. The amount of Antabuse in someone's system then depends on how frequently he takes it (daily, weekly, occasionally) and when he took his last dose (within one day, three days, or 14 days.) In Donald's case, one reason the Antabuse reaction was so strong was that he had been taking Antabuse daily for two weeks. Another reason was that his last dose of Antabuse was shortly before he began drinking.

Some heavy drinkers may not choose to believe how long Antabuse stays in the body. They cite cases of people who drank without ill effects 24 hours after their last dose of Antabuse. Is it possible that someone could do that?

Yes, it is *possible* that someone could drink alcohol 24 hours after taking Antabuse without experiencing an Antabuse reaction. Younger drinkers whose general physical condition (and especially that of their liver) is good *might* be able to drink safely "on top of" Antabuse. In addition, some medications can reduce the severity of an Antabuse reaction. Finally, those who plan to drink often surreptitiously spit out the Antabuse rather than swallow it. As a result, while others might *think* his last dose of Antabuse was only 24 hours prior to his drinking, in fact the drinker may not have had any Antabuse for much longer.

The important thing to remember is that while some few people *might* drink 24 hours after taking Antabuse, no one can plan to drink alcohol *safely* for 14 days after taking his last dose of Antabuse.

Amount of Alcohol

Remember from Chapter 1 that both the amount of alcohol you drink and the amount of time in which you drink it affect the concentration of alcohol in your blood (the Blood Alcohol Concentration, or BAC). The higher the BAC, the more severe the Antabuse reaction. So a person who guzzles down a six-pack of beer will usually have a more severe reaction than someone who sips a shot of whiskey for an hour.

Why would anyone consume a large amount of alcohol when he has Antabuse in his system? As in Donald's case, some people ignore the early signs of an Antabuse reaction. Several drinkers have mentioned that they were not aware of any Antabuse reaction, even though other people may have commented, for example, upon how flushed their faces were. Some drinkers even ignore the nausea and vomiting that can be part of an Antabuse reaction and continue drinking; they assume it is just like their old hangovers. Those who do ignore the early signs do so at their own peril; they usually pay for their gamble with a more severe reaction.

Physical Condition

Before Antabuse is prescribed for anyone, he must have a physical examination which usually includes laboratory tests and often an electrocardiogram (EKG.) The laboratory tests evaluate the condition of the liver and other organs, while the EKG assesses the functioning of the heart. Antabuse is seldom prescribed for someone with a disease of any severity. People with chronic obstructive lung disease, seizure disorders, and liver, heart, or kidney disease, for example, are usually not good candidates for Antabuse. The primary concern is that people with these medical conditions to not have the physical stamina to withstand an Antabuse reaction. Antabuse is also not prescribed for those who are psychotic or those who have organic brain damage, since they lack the ability to make rational decisions about drinking alcohol when taking Antabuse.

Despite all of these precautions, however, some Antabuse patients can have slight impairments in their health which lead to more severe Antabuse reactions. For these people, Antabuse reactions in turn might aggravate their health condition. Donald, for instance, had a mild cardiac condition that did not show up on an EKG, but which nevertheless worsened as a result of the Antabuse reaction. He had a severe Antabuse reaction because he had the worst combination of all three factors affecting the Antabuse reaction: He had been taking Antabuse frequently and had taken a dose recently, he consumed a large quantity of alcohol, and he had a physical condition that heightened the Antabuse reaction.

"INCIDENTAL" ANTABUSE REACTIONS

Some people have heard horror stories about drinkers having Antabuse reactions when they did not drink any alcohol. Chemically, this is impossible, for you must take alcohol into your system in order to have an Antabuse reaction. What can happen, though, is that alcohol can enter your system in a disguised form, as part of either medication or food. The manufacturer of Antabuse, Ayerst Laboratories, has several useful publications available which list all the medications and food preparations of which one must be cautious when taking Antabuse. Ask your doctor for them.

Some foods present little difficulty. When alcohol has been cooked or baked, it usually evaporates. Other foods can present some danger. Brandied desserts such as fruitcake can be problematic since pockets of uncooked alcohol often remain in the food. In addition, people taking Antabuse need to beware of garnishes, such as creme de menthe poured over ice cream. These problems more frequently arise when dining out, rather than at home, since we often cannot know how foods are prepared.

The issue of medications that contain alcohol is an important one. Many over-the-counter medications—especially cough medicines and cold remedies—contain alcohol, sometimes in large proportions. Many mouthwashes are surprisingly high in alcohol content. People taking Antabuse need to read labels for alcohol content or to rely on a pharmacist's advice. If there is any doubt about prescription or non-prescription medication, call the physician who prescribed the Antabuse. In addition, even when your physician prescribes a new medication, it is good to remind him that you are taking Antabuse.

All of these situations presume that you are awake and alert enough to inform your physician. What about the occasions when you have been in an accident and are unconscious or otherwise unable to provide the information? It is for precisely this reason that Ayerst Laboratories distributes a wallet card which you should carry on your person when you are taking Antabuse. This care alerts medical personnel that you are taking Antabuse and should therefore not be given medications containing alcohol. If you prefer, a company named Medicalert makes a badge that serves the same purpose. The same type of badge is used by diabetics and people with drug allergies, so it will not identify you from afar as a problem drinker. The badge can be worn on neck chain or bracelet band.

If you do experience a reaction, you should call the physician who prescribed the Antabuse. He will likely recommend that you go the emergency room of a nearby hospital to be evaluated or treated. If the reaction is severe, you will be treated to restore your blood pressure and to prevent shock. If it is not severe, you will be observed for several hours. Most Antabuse reactions last between one-half and three hours. When the symptoms have subsided, most people feel exhausted. When they awaken after some sleep, the reaction is usually over. Nevertheless, it is important to remember that Antabuse reactions can be quite serious and should be treated as medical emergencies.

WHY ANTABUSE?

Given what has been said so far about side effects, contraindications, and bad reactions, one has to wonder why anyone would use Antabuse or advise others to use it.

The most basic reason is that, for several reasons, it seems to help people stop drinking.

Antabuse Helps Simplify Decisions

People with drinking problems devote a tremendous amount of time to alcohol. There is not only all the time spent drinking and recovering from its effects, but also the time that is spent planning for the drinking. Each day the drinker must make many decisions regarding his drinking—when and where to drink, what to drink, how to get enough money to afford drinking, what alibis to use to camouflage (or at least minimize) the drinking. The large amount of time devoted to these activities is what prompts some to say that problem drinkers are "obsessed" with alcohol.

Unfortunately, the amount of time thinking about alcohol does not always decrease merely because someone stops drinking. The sober person is still confronted by all the old temptations to drink. Instead of focusing a huge amount of time on drinking, the drinker now pours his energy into *not* drinking. This is a horse of a different color, perhaps, but a horse nonetheless. The drinker is still preoccupied with alcohol.

Antabuse provides one alternative to this preoccupation. Dr. Maxwell N. Weisman has put it well: With Antabuse, "instead of having to make thousands of decisions each day not to drink, he makes only one—to take his medication." Many drinkers report a great sense of relief after taking Antabuse. They can then focus their mental energies on how to improve their lives rather than solely on how to resist drinking.

Antabuse Helps People Confront Problems Sober

Some drinkers believe that there are certain things they just cannot do while sober, such as meeting people, disagreeing with the boss, or spending time alone. By taking Antabuse, drinkers *must* confront their problems while sober. They are often pleasantly surprised at how resourceful they can be when sober. The successes they experience while sober can go a long way toward improving the self-confidence and self-esteem they may have lost while drinking.

So there are many ways in which Antabuse can be helpful to a problem drinker. But Antabuse is certainly not "the cure" for problem drinking. Alcoholics Anonymous makes the useful distinction between being "dry" and being "sober." Being "dry" means merely not drinking alcohol. Being "sober," on the other hand, implies changing one's thoughts, feelings, and behavior so that one can cope with the situations that formerly led to excessive drinking.

All Antabuse can do is help someone stay "dry." But by doing so, it can help set the stage for someone to become "sober." Rather than being the "cure" for a drinking problem, Antabuse is one more tool that a person can use in building a lifestyle without alcohol.

Some people wonder how effective Antabuse is in helping people build such a lifestyle. Once again, the best answer seems to be—it depends. Compared to other forms of treatment, Antabuse is sometimes seen as more effective, sometimes less. In one review of research on alcoholism, it was found that treatment programs that used Antabuse tended to have higher success rates than those that did not.

There are two other general findings from research on Antabuse. First, when Antabuse is the *only* form of treatment used, it is not very effective. In this respect Antabuse is similar to other forms of treatment, since successful treatment of alcoholism seems to require a combination of treatment approaches. Second, the effectiveness of Antabuse seems to increase when clients must take it in order to receive—or not lose—things they value. For example, if drinkers must take Antabuse in order to avoid a jail sentence, Antabuse seems to work fairly well. Similarly, those who take Antabuse to retain their jobs seem to get greater benefit than do those who have nothing to lose.

In addition to its being effective in combination with other treatment, there is another reason alcoholism counselors like to use Antabuse—it is often seen as a test of how motivated the drinker is to stop drinking. In particular, it is often chosen as a form of treatment for drinkers who have made previous unsuccessful attempts to stop drinking. Some drinkers need an "enforced" alcohol-free period before they can develop a sober lifestyle.

DECIDING TO TAKE ANTABUSE

If you decide to take Antabuse, there are several things you will need to do.

1. *See your physician.* Assuming that your physician is familiar with Antabuse, he will want to take a medical history, give you a physical examination, and perform the tests we described earlier. Once the results of those tests are returned, he will decide if you can safely take Antabuse. If he concludes you can, he will then describe how Antabuse works and tell you about its side effects. He will probably also give you some literature to read.

2. *Read the literature about Antabuse.* Ayerst Laboratories, the pharmaceutical company that manufactures Antabuse, distributes several pamphlets describing the use of Antabuse. One is called *Now That You're on Antabuse.* This booklet is written in clear language and provides answers to many of the common questions about Antabuse. The Ayerst salesman provides them for physicians, who in turn give them to people taking Antabuse. If your physician does not have a copy of this pamphlet, he may well have some other written description that is equivalent to it. If he does not have any written material, you might want to contact a local alcohol treatment program or the local Area Council on Alcoholism to see if they can provide you with some of the literature. Once you get the literature, *read it.* Many clients skim through the literature without paying great attention to it. Merely skimming it will just make things more difficult for you and for your physician.

3. *Ask questions.* As you read the material, it might be helpful to underline sections you do not understand and write down any questions you have in the margin. That will ensure that you will have all your questions answered when you go to the physician. Do not be afraid to ask the questions that come to your mind. There is no such thing as a stupid question.

4. *Inform the people you live with that you are taking Antabuse.* The primary reason for doing this is so that they will be careful not to serve you food prepared in alcohol. They also need to know what happens during an Antabuse reaction and what measures to take.

A secondary reason for informing those people is that it may make them feel much better. The fact that you have begun taking Antabuse shows that you are willing to take concrete steps to stop your drinking.

5. *Do not drink alcoholic beverages prior to taking your first dose of Antabuse.* Some clients decide to have a "farewell" drink before starting Antabuse. Usually people cannot start Antabuse treatment unless at least 12 hours have passed since their last drink. Tell your physician when your last drink was.

6. *Carry a wallet card.* Ayerst Laboratories distributes a wallet card that you should carry on your person when taking Antabuse. It is primarily designed to alert medical people that you are taking Antabuse. If you prefer, contact Medicalert about the badge we described earlier.

As noted in the beginning of the chapter, Antabuse is not a magical cure for problem drinking. It can, however, be a very useful tool in helping people develop alternative ways of coping with problems. Knowing something about how it works allows you now to evaluate it as one of your options.

PART 3

What Families and
Friends Can Do

Chapter 6

For the Families and Friends of Drinkers

The main reason why it is important for drinkers to get help is something we have already mentioned: Most people who have drinking problems cannot lick them themselves.

When we talk about families and friends of drinkers, however, the main reason *they* need help is to learn how to deal with their reactions to the drinking and the consequences for their relationships with the drinker. When a family goes for help, it is to help the family; whatever effect it has on the drinker is secondary.

Almost always, an important problem accompanies heavy drinking—a problem that may have an impact on the family. Many drinkers do not have a true understanding of their drinking problems, even if others around them see the problems very clearly. This is so in part because heavy drinking tends to reduce people's abilities to judge things accurately. Many heavy drinkers tend to explain their drinking problems away, or rationalize them, or blame them entirely on others, or believe them to be less serious than they really are. Those defenses, and the fact that alcohol may cause some to experience actual memory lapses, may keep drinkers from admitting that they have problems and often help them deny their problems altogether.

Consider Tom, for example. While he was in the hospital, Tom spent most of his time hiding in his room lest any visiting neighbors or friends see him. He was sure that they would be shocked to see him so debilitated, despite the good intentions that might lead them to visit him while he was sick.

Tom's wife laughed and shook her head when his counselor told her about Tom's behavior. "He must think they're blind!" she exclaimed. She explained that Tom was in the habit of visibly stumbling home from the tavern on the corner and crawling up the stairs into the house, *literally* on his hands and knees—and that was on the good nights, when he made it under his own power. Sometimes he fell into a drunken sleep on the front lawn. On those occasions his teenage sons would carry him into the house in full view of the neighbors. Tom was part of the neighborhood folklore. Everyone knew about him. Only Tom did not know that they knew—or at least he did not want to admit to himself that they knew.

Since they often cannot appreciate the true extent of their problems, many heavy drinkers do not understand how important it is for them to get help. So they do not go for help. It is often difficult—and sometimes impossible—to convince a drinker to go for treatment if he flatly and consistently denies he has a problem. When this happens, it usually means that the drinker is not yet ready to accept help, and the efforts of those close to the drinker to convince him to get treatment will probably be in vain.

Whatever the reasons underlying a person's drinking and whatever its course, one thing is clear: A person's drinking problem affects those close to him, and it probably has affected you. Friends and family often have mixed emotional reactions to a loved one's drinking. On the one hand, the consequences can make you angry, and understandably so. Drinking consumes larger and larger amounts of money, time, and energy, leaving less of all of these for the drinker's loved ones. That can hurt deeply. But, on the other hand, precisely because you *do* care about the drinker, you may also want to help him, irrespective of the hurt or anger you might feel. Helping the drinker might, in the long-run, be helping yourself as well. We know that, after treatment, drinkers who return to families in which there is less conflict and more mutual support among members function better and are less prone to return to drinking.

Let us talk now about what you can do to help yourself in this difficult situation.

WHAT CAN FAMILY MEMBERS AND FRIENDS DO?

First of all, family members need to recognize their own emotional reactions to the problem drinker and the upset caused by him. Some are angry or resentful and ask, "Why should I do anything to help?" Still others feel guilty and think that drinking problems arose because of some failure on their part.

All of these feelings are normal and should not be ignored. The feelings need to be discussed among the family members (perhaps with the aid of a counselor) so that the drinker can be dealt with effectively.

In addition to understanding the emotional reactions, there are certain "dos and don'ts" you can use as guidelines to help the problem drinker. You may want to discuss these guidelines among members of the family so that you can arrive at a consistent approach. The more consistent the approach, the greater the chances that you will be successful in helping the problem drinker.

Dos

There are four major things you can do in your efforts to help the drinker. First, *learn as much as you can about problem drinking and alcoholism.* At the end of the book we have included some good sources of information on alcoholism. Alcohol treatment facilities in your area may sponsor lecture series you can attend. You might want to seek out their staff members to ask questions or seek their advice. In addition, self-help groups such as Alcoholics Anonymous, Al-Anon, and Alateen can provide lots of information through their meetings and their literature. (More about them in the next chapter.)

The more you understand about the problem, and the drinker's view of it, from outside sources, the better you will be able to do the second thing: *Try to get the drinker to get treatment.* He might not be able to get help on his own. He might need your assistance. It is important that you be there to help the drinker when he wants to change.

The third thing you can do to help the problem drinker is to *continue to show him that you are concerned about the drinking problem once he goes for treatment.* Some families see the drinker's entering treatment as the only goal. "Thank God for a little peace," they may say. Remember, though, that he must successfully *complete* treatment for your life with him truly to change. So you can encourage the drinker to complete treatment. Be involved in his treatment. Do whatever you can to make his treatment successful.

The fourth thing you can do is to *get better yourself.* Families of drinkers often live chaotic, confusing, and unpredictable lives. All interested family members need to join together in an effort to create healthier lives for themselves, *even if the drinker chooses not to get help.* Find out about how families can change, what they can do to take a first step, and how they recover.

A comprehensive, step-by-step approach to family recovery is presented in a book entitled *Taking Charge: How Families Can Climb Out of the Chaos of Addiction . . . and Flourish.* The approach in *Taking Charge* can help you begin your journey to family health.

Don'ts

Just as there are things you *should* do to help someone with a drinking problem, there are also things you *should not* do. First among them is *not to protect the drinker from the consequences of his drinking.* Treatment tends to be more successful when the drinker recognizes that drinking is a problem for him. That recognition is postponed when people "protect" the drinker. So do not call in sick for him when he is too hung over to get to work. Try to be as honest as you can with family members and close friends. If he doesn't accompany you to a family affair and you are asked why, tell the truth. You can say something like "He decided to go out drinking instead."

Being straightforward with family members and close friends will probably not be as painful and cruel as it may sound to you now. Very likely, they know about the drinking—and, if they do not know, they may have their suspicions. In any case, his drinking is not a reflection on you, and keeping the "secret" may only encourage him to keep drinking.

Second, *do not argue about the drinking problem.* A simple statement—"You are drinking too much; I think you need some help"—is sufficient. Arguments rarely result in the positive change you are seeking. It is important to avoid arguments when a person is drunk. In that state, he cannot discuss issues rationally, probably will not remember what was said, and might become violent.

Christopher was the most original case example of this from among the people we have treated recently. When Christopher began treatment, he had not had a drink in several months. Prior to his decision to stop drinking, his wife had begun to make comments about his drinking much more often than she had in previous years. She also drank, but her drinking had not been a point of contention.

Not, that is, until Christopher stopped drinking and began to realize that his wife drank quite a bit more than he had been aware of previously. So he began to broach the topic with her, but his attempts to talk about *her* drinking seemed to lead to arguments. He began to question his evalution of the amount she drank and how it affected her, and he stopped bringing it up.

But he did not stop thinking about it. In fact, he began to keep track of her liquor purchases. He kept a record of the bottles she bought and the ones she threw out. He kept a log of the times she complained that she did not have enough money for groceries. After a while, he concluded that his original hunches were accurate—she did, indeed, drink too much, and it did interfere with her actions and with family finances.

Christopher knew that he would have to reintroduce the topic of her drinking again if he was to have any chance of influencing her. But he knew that when he talked to her, arguments resulted, and arguments did not lead anywhere. So he decided to write her a letter. The letter carefully explained his concern about her drinking. He left it for her to read; she read it, but she did not mention a word about it. And she did not change her drinking.

Christopher then elected to try again. In his second letter, however, he explained in detail his observations, reiterated his concern, and offered to talk to her about her drinking if she wanted to. This letter elicited a reaction and a change in her drinking. The key was that Christopher had set things up so that the opportunity for arguing was removed, and his wife's response could not shift attention from the matter at hand—her drinking. The letter had succeeded where the arguments had failed.

The third thing not to do is an offshoot of number two. In the heat of an argument, many people make threats—"I'll have you put away," "I'll kill you if you do that again." A general piece of advice is: Do not threaten. On the one hand, *do not threaten what you cannot deliver.* "I'll have you put away," you might shout. While you well may want to do so, chances are slim that you can pull it off. An empty threat makes the drinker doubt your effectiveness. On the other hand, if your threat is something you could really carry out—filing for divorce, leaving home—*do not threaten unless you intend to follow through.* In other words, do not try to bluff. Threats you could follow through on, but do not, become background music to some drinkers. Only threaten divorce, for instance, if you have firmly concluded it is the best move for you under the circumstances and only if you are willing to take some concrete action, such as seeing an attorney.

Fourth, *do not try bribing the drinker.* Bribery is probably even less effective than threats. Take Joe's case: He was as avid a drinker as he was a tennis player. His wife Alice worked for a sporting goods firm. She offered the following deal: If he would stop drinking, she would arrange for him to attend several tennis clinics conducted by top pros. It seemed to work. Joe stayed sober and enjoyed the first two clinics. It was hard to tell how he felt about the third because he came home two days late, drunk and disheveled.

Fifth, *do not accept responsibility for the drinker's behavior*. "It's all your fault," you may hear; "If only you weren't so bossy/a pushover/so homely/so pretty/so stupid/a know-it-all." No matter how guilty you may feel, you did not force the drinker to drink—he did that all by himself. And just as his drinking is his responsibility, so is his sobriety. You can help, but you cannot do it all.

Finally, *do not stop attending treatment*, including Al-Anon, if he returns to drinking. You are going for treatment in order to help *yourself* get better, whether or not the drinker improves. Some spouses say, "I really don't need any treatment, but I'll go if it will help him." If you put on this air of false nobility, you are not being truthful with yourself.

If you are "going for him," it is to help him stay sober. That is nice, and it is important, but it is not enough. Equally important is that his staying sober makes *your* life better. And that is the reason a drinker's family—you— goes for treatment.

The family may need some assistance in order to deal effectively with the drinker and his problems, even if the drinker declines treatment or if he does not complete treatment successfully. Quite often the problem drinker rather substantially disrupts the family's life. This may include disruption of the social and economic situation of the family, but it also includes disruption of the psychological well-being of the family. For this, the family itself may benefit from help. *Taking Charge*, the book we mentioned earlier in this chapter, is a good resource guide for family recovery.

TREATMENT OF DRINKING-RELATED
FAMILY PROBLEMS

The drinker can affect the lives of his family quite apart from other difficulties in the family. Living with a problem drinker is never easy. The family might need help to learn to understand and live with the problem drinking. This is best done when family members can come to understand their values about and attitudes toward alcohol and drinking in general and the loved one's problem in particular. It is often done with the drinker as part of the overall treatment program.

Though family members might be reluctant to blame the drinker directly for the problems he causes, they cannot help but have their own emotional reactions to the upset caused by him.

Sometimes people feel a bit guilty when they discover they have feelings of anger, hurt, frustration, and embarrassment. "After all," some people reason, "shouldn't we be *helping* the drinker?" Well, the important things to remember are these: First, such feelings are normal. Many people have them. Second, they should not be ignored or put aside. Families are best able to deal with the drinking problems of their relatives when they can deal as well with their own emotional reactions to those problems. This will enable family members to understand their relationships with the drinker.

Third, family members may have to learn how relationships with the drinker might change if he undergoes treatment—or, as sometimes happens, if he does *not* undergo treatment. Both of these possibilities can require the family to adjust. If the drinker undergoes treatment, family members might find that he will begin to re-enter the family as a full member. This might require a period of adjustment for the family. The family might have become accustomed to functioning with the drinker as only a partial member. If the drinker refuses treatment, family members might have to learn how to function in a manner that is adequate for them without the drinker. Neither will be an easy task for you.

"THREE Rs" FOR THE DRINKER'S SPOUSE

There is little doubt that abusive drinking imposes tremendous financial, social, and emotional burdens on drinkers' families. Perhaps these burdens are felt most wrenchingly by their spouses. For them, as for drinkers, the trauma caused by the abusive behavior frequently does not resolve itself when the drinking stops. The drinker's spouse then experiences the Three Rs.

Retribution

When the drinking stops, non-drinking spouses often want to inflict pain on drinkers to make up for their own sufferings during the period of heavy drinking. Sometimes, though, people do not want to come to terms openly with their vengefulness. Many people think vengeance is "not nice," and they shun any hint of it in themselves. But it is often a reality where drinking is concerned.

When it is recognized, the desire is hard to fulfill. The feeling of retribution is often expressed in vague terms that do not translate easily to appropriate means of execution. In some cases, though, the fantasy can play itself out in a rather demonstrative fashion.

Consider the case of the N.'s. When they were referred for marital counseling, Mr. N. had been steadily increasing his drinking for 11 years. Three months before referral, he had been treated in an alcoholism treatment program, and he was attending Alcoholics Anonymous (AA) meetings regularly. Mrs. N. had been attending Al-Anon meetings since her husband's enrollment in alcoholism treatment. Together they were interested in resolving longstanding marital difficulties, some of which were related to his drinking.

Counseling commenced after three evaluation sessions, but progress was very slow and difficult. Mrs. N. directed most of the attention of the first four counseling sessions to her husband's past drinking escapades and particularly to their effects on her and their two adolescent children. Soon, Mr. N. complained about her "always harping on things that I can't change now and I told you I was sorry for." He was frustrated that his replies did not satisfy his wife. Mrs. N. became progressively angrier at her husband's apologies, saying that it was "easy for you to say that now. You didn't go through what we went through."

Mr. N. started session eight with a challenge to his wife to explain "incontrovertible evidence I have that you're having an affair" with a man she had met at work some years before. Mrs. N. confirmed the evidence, verifying both that she had seen him three times over the previous three weeks and that she had been quite indiscreet in her liaison with him. She added that she "lost interest in it when I knew you found out about us."

At the end of the eighth session, both were very angry, and Mr. N. made an elaborate point of telling his wife "how hurt I am that you would do this to me." In the ninth session, they talked about Mrs. N.'s affair in terms of her overwhelming "need to get back at you. You hurt us so much I couldn't bear it." The need was satisfied, she said, when she was sure Mr. N. had found out about the brief affair.

Clearly, the N.'s present a graphic—though somewhat extreme—illustration of this issue. A less dramatic, and perhaps more typical example is the case of the C.'s The C.'s were married for eight years at the time Mrs. C. stopped drinking. Two months thereafter she came with her husband for marriage counseling. One of the first issues to arise was Mrs. C.'s observation that, though they had enjoyed an active and satisfying life together in the past, their lives now were being smothered by Mr. C.'s curtailment of their social activities. When Mrs. C. suggested an activity, she said, "He vetoes it. He says, 'We can't do that. What if you drink again?'" She interpreted his explanations as "hurtful" because they deprived her of activities she enjoyed. To which he replied, "How is that different from all the times we *did* go out and you got so drunk you made a spectacle of yourself in front of all those people?" This exchange launched the couple into a discussion of the underlying issue at hand: how important (and uncharacteristic) it had been for him to think about inflicting reciprocal pain on his wife.

In general, efforts to resolve retribution feelings usually are most productive when they focus on reducing the issue to its concrete implications. This is usually a two-step process. Initially, spouses evaluate whether retribution is *possible*, first by considering what form it would have to take to be satisfying and then by contemplating how it could be accomplished. This examination usually leads to the conclusion that retribution is not possible as fantasized, however compelling the fantasy may be.

Later, aggrieved spouses consider whether retribution is *desirable*, however possible it may seem, given the chance that is could have a further destructive impact on the marital relationship. Most often the conclusion is that retribution is undesirable (and impossible to obtain), and it is resolved by "writing off the pain," perhaps in return for acknowledgment of its legitimacy and some protection against its recurrence.

Restitution

Nondrinking spouses frequently have a hope for "repayment" for their sufferings. Unlike the issue of retribution, people are usually willing to talk about this hope. The manner in which such restitution can be made, however, is not always clear. While the wish for "repayment" may be clear, it is usually expressed in vague emotional terms that cannot be reduced to a specific currency. As a result, ex-drinkers often express frustration that the ill-defined expectation cannot be met.

For example, one woman described her husband's expectation as "demands I can't meet. How can I pay you for what you went through? What's the price? It's like blackmail, emotional blackmail" for which the ransom cannot be defined concretely. Ultimately, this couple resolved the issue by working out a set of agreements about their mutual contributions to each other's future needs. That process, the husband later said, helped him in two ways. On the one hand, he could "expect things to improve emotionally in the future." On the other, he was able to "end my futile search" with the conclusion that ultimately he could not be "repaid" for his past sufferings: The emotional means for meeting his expectation simply did not exist.

Refuge

The desire for refuge—protection against future disruptions from a spouse's return to drinking—comes to the fore when spouses have resolved the first two Rs. Nondrinking spouses then usually insist on some assurance that their immediate future will be fairly secure from major disruption. Especially in cases in which the ex-drinker has suffered lapses in the past, refuge may be a primary concern for the non-drinking spouse.

Refuge is an elusive quarry, though. After all is said and done, the ex-drinker cannot offer much more than a promise that he will not start drinking again. And for many couples, promises are not impressive commodities. The T.'s, however, took such a promise a step further.

Mr. T. had been drinking for 17 years when he entered a detoxification and rehabilitation program. He did so after promising his wife—in front of the judge officiating at the divorce hearing she had initiated—that he would seek treatment for his drinking problem. His wife agreed to postpone that proceeding if he met one condition; in her words, "I need some protection."

Mr. T. agreed, and the following week they signed an agreement, prepared by her attorney, which provided that he would automatically forfeit claims to the house and family car and to custody of the children and that the divorce proceedings would be reinstituted automatically if he took even one drink after he entered treatment. Though this agreement is extreme, it allowed Mrs. T. some comfort in the knowledge that "at least I know you have something riding on it if you decide to go back to the booze. You know, your word hasn't been worth much in the past. I can't really trust you about your drinking. Maybe this will make you think." The agreement allowed Mrs. T. at least some confidence that she was "protected" from a repeat of her sufferings.

In the main, the issue of protection usually does not present itself in such stark proportions as it did with the T.'s. But, in some form, the "Catch-22" quality usually does: "I require a guarantee from you, but I can't trust any guarantee you give me." The resolution for most couples is to reach a willingness to live with some uncertainty in their relationships.

The Three Rs are important parts of a husband's or wife's reaction to a drinking spouse once the drinking has stopped. Although most non-drinking spouses have reacted emotionally to each stage of the drinker's alcoholism, the Three Rs usually come together only after the drinking stops and it is time to put things back together. Often for a marriage, the process of repair, and the process of working through the Three Rs, cannot be done alone. Sometimes it is a good idea to seek the help of a marriage counselor.

MARRIAGE COUNSELING

A very important part of treatment for a drinker's alcohol problems often involves the drinker's spouse. This is usually called Marriage Counseling or Marital Therapy or Couples Therapy, and it is sometimes a branch of Family Counseling. This is not to say that people's spouses drive them to drink. It is only to say that a person's drinking usually affects those close to him. So part of the treatment logically may include those close to him.

In marriage counseling, you will have the oportunity to discuss difficulties in your marriage from *your* perspective. You will also have an opportunity to hear your spouse's perspective. The marriage counselors are there to help the two of you work your difficulties out.

Sometimes the difficulties follow from the drinking, and sometimes the difficulties are caused by the drinking. Whatever the case, it is often hard for two people to work out their difficulties alone. Differences may arise because each person has his own viewpoint on things, and neither can see areas of potential compromise, so it helps to have trained "outsiders" help both partners understand what is going on between them and how to work things out.

Take the case of Carl and Shirley: Carl and Shirley had been married for 38 years when Carl decided to get some help for his drinking problem. He had been drinking for 32 years, heavily for 12, with several short periods of sobriety. None of his children could remember a time when Carl had not been drinking, and the two youngest virtually had known him only drunk. Shortly before the start of treatment, Shirley filed for and obtained a divorce from Carl, saying that she could no longer abide the promises, the drunken behavior, and the embarrassment.

Soon after Carl was discharged from an inpatient alcoholism rehabilitation program, Shirley and Carl decided to come for treatment of their problems together. Perhaps something of their relationship could be salvaged, they reasoned.

Shirley viewed her divorce from Carl as a step she had to take after so many let-downs over the years. She could not be sure that this time Carl was serious about treatment. Divorce was her protection against future disappointments.

At the same time, however, Carl and Shirley wanted to reconstruct the shattered portions of their marriage. They lived together as a family with their children, they made family plans together, and they both came for marriage counseling.

It was hard for Carl and Shirley to start talking about their problems with their counselor. Carl was very remorseful about the effect his drinking had had on Shirley. Shirley was quite angry about the suffering and responsibility she had had to bear during Carl's drinking years. As counseling progressed, she realized that she was not only angry; she also wanted some form of restitution for her pains over the years. As we saw previously, this is not an uncommon reaction among families of drinkers.

As counseling continued, Shirley concluded that Carl

could not make meaningful restitution to her. After all, she concluded, what could he do or say that would really make up for all those years? But she also concluded that she wanted some protection for herself and the children in the event Carl was not successful this time around. The divorce was protection enough, she decided.

From that point, the marriage counseling focused on the way Carl and Shirley communicated with each other, the difficulty they had expressing their feelings to each other and the children, and the expectations each had of the other for the relationship in general.

Carl eventually found work after being unemployed for a year and, with both salaries, Carl and Shirley were able to pay off their bills and begin to enjoy some of the luxuries that had been out of their reach for so long.

Equally important, both Carl and Shirley also reported that the quality of their relationship improved. They enjoyed each other's company once more, and they were able to share their feelings with each other and the children. After 18 months of counseling, Carl had a brief slip, which they resolved—together—in one day.

At this time, four years after marriage counseling began, Carl and Shirley have finished counseling and are talking about remarrying.

TREATMENT FOR OTHER FAMILY PROBLEMS

Sometimes the problems a drinker's family experiences are the result of some rather serious family problems that would exist even if there were no drinker in the family. When this is the case, families may need help in order to function better, especially since the problems usually do not get much better even if the drinking family member gets help.

Help for families is available from a number of sources. Hospitals and community clinics that have alcoholism facilities frequently have programs for families. These may include lectures or seminars for families to learn about alcohol and alcoholism. They may also include family counseling programs to help families of drinkers in treatment. These may suffice. But families with more basic problems may require specialized family counseling programs which go beyond the counseling offered in alcoholism treatment facilities. Such specialized programs can be found in clinics around the country, and the staff of the alcoholism programs can usually refer you to them.

WHAT ABOUT SLIPS?

When someone slips, those close to the drinker can help. Family members and friends can help in much the same way as they may have helped when drinking first became a problem. They can learn about the problem of slips, try to persuade the drinker to return for more help for the drinking problem, and offer the drinker support for his efforts to seek additional help.

An important point to remember is that slips are not uncommon. As we mentioned in the previous chapter, many people who have been treated for drinking problems slip and return to drinking after treatment. *A slip does not necessarily seal the drinker's fate.* It does not necessarily mean that he will never be able to stop drinking and deal with his problems. Though it is often painful and discouraging, it can be a learning experience for the drinker. Don is a good case in point. What would you do it he were *your* relative?

Don was a heavy drinker for many years. He had participated in an inpatient rehabilitation program in order to stop drinking. He continued treatment in an outpatient treatment program and stayed sober for two years.

One evening he was invited to a retirement dinner and was seated at the head table. When asked if he would like a pre-dinner drink, Don automatically ordered a martini. He drank it, then ordered and drank a second. He was enjoying himself greatly and had just ordered a third when he realized what he had done, that he had started drinking again after almost two years. He got scared. But instead of dwelling on the alcohol or on some "compulsion" to drink,

Don took matters into his own hands. He excused himself from the dinner, went home, went to bed, and called the treatment center the next morning. For insurance—and after talking it over with his counselor—he decided to take Antabuse again for a week. Drinking the martinis did not lead to an overwhelming desire to continue drinking. Don had caught himself.

Friends and family members are often in good positions to help the drinker learn from his slip and to influence his return to treatment. They can offer the drinker a slightly different—and often more objective—view of what was happening in the period before the slip. Their observations can be invaluable aids for the drinker in his efforts to figure out why he slipped. Their concern and close personal relationships with the drinker allow them to help him keep the slip in perspective and to steer him back to treatment. With their support, the drinker might be less resistant to return to treatment.

A slip usually has an emotional impact on those close to the drinker. While they might be very supportive of the drinker, they also may feel quite angry, frustrated, hurt, or embarrassed when the drinking resumes. They sometimes feel responsible for the slip. The same feelings that confronted them initially now return to affect them again.

In addition, family members frequently find it difficult to invest as much trust in the drinker as they did before the slip. This is a response often resented by the drinker, but it remains a problem that must be resolved.

Family members often find themselves in a bind after a slip. The drinker needs the help of those close to him in order to return to treatment and tackle the drinking problem again. But family members and friends need help, too, and drinkers are not able to offer those close to them the support *they* need to deal with the emotions stirred up in them by the slip. Consequently, family members need to look elsewhere for that support. Where could you turn for support were you to find yourself in this predicament? Perhaps some of the resources we mentioned earlier or those in Appendix A at the end of this book would be helpful.

Chapter 7

Al-Anon

Al-Anon is the organization for the relatives of drinkers. Its primary focus is not on helping its members learn to deal with their drinking relatives, but rather on learning about themselves and their reactions to the relatives. Thus, a member should receive the same amount of attention whether the relative is currently drinking or is sober.

Although now a separate organization, Al-Anon began as an outgrowth of Alcoholics Anonymous (see Chapter 4). The initial AA meetings were held in members' homes. The family of the member often accompanied him to the meeting. While waiting for the meeting to end, members' relatives sat together and talked among themselves. These discussions yielded two important points; (1) the relatives shared a common problem of how to live with a drinker and (2) not all family problems stemmed from the drinking. The relatives thought they needed help with their problems and thought that the AA self-help format could be adapted to meet their needs.

The AA Auxiliary, the forerunner of Al-Anon, was formed in 1941. By 1949, 87 groups applied for listing in the AA directory. At that time it was decided that the group needed to establish a separate identity so that people would not confuse it with AA. As a result, the organization adopted the name Al-Anon and formed its own information clearinghouse and directory. In 1954, Al-Anon incorporated its directory service, newsletter, and publication of books and pamphlets into a nonprofit organization called Al-Anon Family Group Headquarters. Today, Al-Anon is an international organization with thousands of affiliated groups.

MEETINGS

Al-Anon meetings are patterned after AA meetings and, like them, can vary greatly in their individual structures. A general model or blueprint for an Al-Anon meeting is provided in Al-Anon's book *Living with an Alcoholic*.

There are two general types of Al-Anon meetings, "open" and "closed." *Open* meetings are ones any interested member of the community can attend. Their purpose is to educate the audience about alcoholism in general, and the role of Al-Anon in particular. At these meetings, it is customary to have a speaker (frequently an Al-Anon or AA member, clergyman, or mental health professional) address the group or for an appropriate film to be shown.

Attendance at a closed meeting is restricted to members and potential members. At a closed meeting, some form of both the Preamble and the Welcome are read. An example of each follows:

Preamble

The Al-Anon Family Groups are a fellowship of relatives and friends of alcoholics who share their experience, strength, and hope in order to solve their common problems of living with an alcoholic, and to help others do the same. We believe alcoholism is an illness which can be arrested, and that changed family attitudes can often aid recovery.

The only requirement for membership is that there be a relative or friend with a drinking problem. There are no dues for membership. Al-Anon is self-supporting through its own voluntary contributions.

Al-Anon is not allied with any sect, denomination, political entity, organization, or institution; does not engage in any controversy; neither endorses not opposes any cause. Our primary purpose is to practice the Al-Anon program so that we may help others with similar problems, to aid the alcoholic through understanding, and to grow spiritually ourselves.

Welcome

We welcome you to the *(name of group)* Al-Anon Family Group, and hope you will find in this fellowship the help and friendship we have been privileged to enjoy.

We who live with the problem of alcoholism understand as perhaps few others can. We, too, were lonely and frustrated, but in Al-Anon we discover that no situation is really hopeless, and that it is possible for us to find contentment, and even happiness, whether the alcoholic is still drinking or not.

We urge you to try our program. It will show you how to find solutions that lead to serenity. So much depends on our own attitudes, and as we learn to place our problem in its true perspective, we find it loses its power to dominate our thoughts and our lives.

The family situation is bound to improve as we apply the Al-Anon ideas. Without such spiritual help, living with an alcoholic is too much for most of us. Our thinking becomes distorted by trying to force solutions and we become irritable and unreasonable without knowing it.

The Al-Anon program is based on the Twelve Steps of AA which we try, little by little, one day at a time, to apply to our lives, along with our slogans and the Serenity Prayer. The loving interchange of help among members and daily reading of Al-Anon literature thus makes us ready to receive the priceless gift of serenity.

The structure of a closed meeting can vary greatly, but usually some form of group discussion takes place.

The theme of an Al-Anon meeting might be one of the Twelve Steps, an Al-Anon slogan, or a topic suggested in Al-Anon literature. The goal of the meeting is to have members share personal experiences and become actively involved with each other.

AL-ANON'S STRUCTURE

Al-Anon's Twelve Traditions describe the policies and guidelines under which Al-Anon meetings are conducted. The Twelve Traditions are as follows:

1. Our common welfare should come first: personal progress for the greatest number depends upon unity.

2. For our group purpose there is but one authority— a loving God as he may express Himself in our group conscience. Our leaders are trusted servants—they do not govern.

3. The relatives of alcoholics, when gathered together for mutual aid, may call themselves an Al-Anon Family Group, provided that, as a group, they have no other affiliation. The only requirement for membership is that there be a problem of alcoholism in a relative or friend.

4. Each group should be autonomous, except in matters affecting another group or Al-Anon or AA, as a whole.

5. Each Al-Anon Family Group has but one purpose: to help families of alcoholics. We do this by practicing the Twelve Steps of AA *ourselves*, by encouraging and understanding our alcoholic relatives, and by welcoming and giving comfort to families of alcoholics.

6. Our Family Groups ought never endorse, finance, or lend our name to any outside enterprise, lest problems of money, property, and prestige divert us from our primary spiritual aim. Although a separate entity, we should always cooperate with Alcoholics Anonymous.

7. Every group ought to be fully self-supporting, declining outside contributions.

8. Al-Anon Twelfth Step work should remain forever nonprofessional, but our service centers may employ special workers.

9. Our groups, as such, ought never be organized, but we may create service boards or committees directly responsible to those they serve.

10. The Al-Anon Family Groups have no opinion on outside issues; hence our name ought never be drawn into public controversy.

11. Our public relations policy is based on attraction rather than promotion; we need always maintain personal anonymity at the level of press, radio, films, and TV. We need guard with special care the anonymity of all AA members.

12. Anonymity is the spiritual foundation of all our Traditions, ever reminding us to place principles above personalities.

These principles are explained in detail in Al-Anon's book *Twelve Steps and Twelve Traditions*, published in 1983 in New York by the Al-Anon Family Group Headquarters.

Al-Anon models itself on Alcoholics Anonymous and utilizes the basic AA method (see Chapter 4). In *Living with an Alcoholic*, Al-Anon acknowledges its use of the AA format, and especially the Twelve Steps; "So universal was the inspiration by which the steps were originally written that Al-Anon, in adopting them to its use, changed only a single word; in the Twelfth Step, the word 'alcoholic' becomes 'others'." The Twelve Steps of AA can be found in Chapter 4.

Al-Anon describes itself as a "spiritual" program of recovery that is implemented by the Twelve Steps. As we discussed in Chapter 4, the Twelve Steps represent four stages of the recovery process: *Surrender, Assessment, Making Amends* and *Carrying the Message to Others*.

Sandy's experience in Al-Anon will help illustrate

progress through these four stages. Sandy had been married to Bill for 11 years when she decided to attend her first Al-Anon meeting. Friends had told her about Al-Anon several years before, and a close friend had been a member for several years. Bill had been drinking since they had started dating. On their first date, he had gotten drunk enough for Sandy to consider not accepting his invitation for the second date. His drinking had increased in the five years before she went to Al-Anon, and it had been the source of much anguish and embarrassment for Sandy and their two children.

Surrender

This first stage of recovery in Al-Anon stresses that a person cannot control a relative's actions, including his or her drinking, and that increased reliance on an Al-Anon group for support is a healthy step on the road to recovery for non-drinking relatives.

At this point, Sandy acknowledged her long-standing hope that she could get Bill to stop drinking if only she tried hard enough. She had tried threats, promises, tears, tantrums, covering for him, and pouring out his liquor. She came to Al-Anon to learn more about his problems.

Assessment

In the assessment stage of recovery, denial can be a problem. Often family members deny the extent of the drinker's problems with alcohol and the extent to which those problems have damaged the family. As they move past some of their denial of the extent of their and the drinker's problems, they frequently confront the true extent of their pent-up rage. Al-Anon is a good place for family members to assess the Three Rs we discussed in Chapter 6.

In addition, in this stage of recovery, family members can determine how they have been involved with the drinker in unhealthy ways. Frequently, family members have sacrificed some measure of family health as they have adjusted their lives to the chaotic circumstances drinkers produce in their families.

At this point, Sandy acknowledged that her well-meaning efforts had failed. She became acutely aware of her anger at and mistrust of Bill. She was able to identify with other group members when they described their chaotic family lives. She was able to identify that covering up for Bill humiliated and frustrated her. She could see that her desperate threats frightened the children.

Making Amends

Alcoholism in a family consumes much of family members' attention and energy. When attention is so focused on drinking, other things are neglected (e.g., personal needs, relationships, health routines). In this stage of recovery in Al-Anon, members might make a list of neglected people and functions and make amends. "Amends" means redirecting energy and attention in a positive manner to renew and maintain neglected relationships and health lifestyles.

At first Sandy was embarrassed to tally up the amount of her time and attention she had devoted to Bill's drinking. Gradually, she was able to talk about her embarrassment with other group members. She remembered her son's last birthday party, when Bill broke the television and smashed a mirror. She threatened divorce, humiliated her son, and the birthday party ended prematurely and on a sad note. Sandy talked to her son about her sorrow and humiliation and planned a "safe" party for his upcoming birthday.

Carrying the Message to Others

In this final stage of recovery in Al-Anon, members reach out to others in earlier stages of their work in Al-Anon. This sort of activity is part of redirecting family members' energy after ending their obsession with their relatives' drinking.

Sandy remembered how hard it had been for her to get started in Al-Anon. She began to come early to meetings to greet new members and to help them feel comfortable enough to discuss their own experiences openly. One new member told Sandy that "your warmth helped me over the rough spots". Sandy felt useful and appreciated at this stage, despite the fact that Bill was still drinking.

AL-ANON AND PROFESSIONAL HELP

In Sandy's case, Al-Anon was crucial in helping her face her family's problems. However, as she came to see her problems more clearly, she decided to seek the help of a psychologist. She continued attending Al-Anon meetings while she worked with the therapist to resolve complex personal and family problems which her Al-Anon friends agreed required professional help.

Sandy's decision to see the psychologist is consistent with Al-Anon's belief that group members not try to offer professional counseling to others. Al-Anon encourages its members to seek professional help for problems that require more than group support. In many cases, Al-Anon membership and professional help work very well together.

Alateen and Alatot

Alateen and Alatot are family support groups for teenagers and for pre-teens, respectively. They are modeled after Al-Anon and adopt Al-Anon's structure and goals to these two groups of family members. Alateen and Alatot meetings are less available than Al-Anon meetings. These two groups were conceived to meet the specialized needs of young children of drinkers.

We will now turn our attention to another group affected by alcoholism, adult children of drinkers.

Chapter 8

Adult Children of Alcoholics*

The problems people experience in adulthood as a result of growing up in a household with parents who drink abusively have been the focus of a great deal of recent attention. The results of research studies and the impressions of many counselors suggest that adult children of alcoholic parents (ACOAs) are more likely than those of non-alcoholic parents to experience a number of difficulties. These include an increased risk of developing alcoholism themselves, difficulty identifying and expressing their emotions, trouble establishing and maintaining satisfying relationships with others, a greater chance of becoming depressed, and posssibly greater tendencies to think about or attempt suicide.

In addition, some researchers have concluded that the impact a parent's abusive drinking has on children varies according to several criteria. For example, in a work published in 1982, Dr. Hesselbrock and colleagues suggested that children who grow up with alcoholism present on *both* sides of the family are more likely to experience more se-

*We are indebted to Margaret Easley for use of ideas and findings contained in her Masters Thesis entitled "Coping with Stress in a Family with an Alcoholic Member" (University of Maryland, 1988).

vere consequences than those with the problem on only one side or those without alcoholism in the family. Dr. Robert Ackerman wrote about his clinical observations of alcoholic families in 1986 and concluded that members of these families can be affected by the alcoholism in different ways depending on three variables: how the drinker responded to alcohol (e.g., was the drinker nasty, jolly, or withdrawn while drinking?), the degree of alcohol abuse (e.g., how severe was the drinking problem?), and each family member's private assessment of how harmful the drinking was to him or her.

Most of the research conducted to investigate the status of children of drinkers has zeroed in on the negative consequences of a parent's drinking. Some of those consequences are physical. There seems to be agreement in many quarters that alcoholism brings an increased risk of physical and sexual assault to the family, primarily by the drinker, and a whole host of problems that can involve the police and courts.

Other consequences can be emotional and intellectual. A series of studies has suggested that, compared to children growing up in non-alcoholic homes, children of abusive drinkers as a group may have more temper tantrums, be excessively aggressive, have learning problems, get into fights with other children more easily, have trouble expressing their feelings, and experience more psychological and social problems.

THE FAMILIES OF ACOAs

A number of authors agree that alcoholic households are homes in which confusion, unpredictability, and chaos reign. An early study (by Dr. Holden in 1945) found that up to one-quarter of the children and adolescents seen at a child guidance clinic had an alcoholic parent. This early finding hinted that alcoholism might have effects that went beyond the drinker and affected the lives of family members.

One of the first detailed descriptions of these fami-

lies came in 1954. In her studies of how families adjust
to the crises alcoholism brings to the family's life, Dr.
Janet Jackson described seven steps that these families go
through as they wrestle with the impact of the drinking in
their midst:

Step 1: Family members attempt to deny that they
have problems, or that the problems are as bad as they appear to be to outsiders.

Step 2: Family members admit that they have problems and try to eliminate those problems, often at great ex-
pense to their emotional well-being.

Step 3: Family members stop trying to control the
drinker and his drinking and try to relieve the tension
caused by the drinking.

Step 4: Family members try to reorganize the family
in spite of the problems that affect the family.

Step 5: Family members try to escape the problems.

Step 6: Family members reorganize the willing members of the family into a healthier family.

Step 7: The whole family recovers from the impact of
the drinking and the whole family reorganizes itself for a
healthier family life.

In his 1982 book entitled *Broken Bottles, Broken
Dreams*, Dr. Deutsch described five attributes of families
with one or more abusive drinkers:

1. The family focuses a large amount of its energies on
the alcoholism, which is the basis of much of the interactions among family members.

2. Family members and the drinker deny that the
drinking is a problem, although family members feel
ashamed of the drinking in their midst.

3. Family members feel insecure because they cannot
predict when or how the drinker might change abruptly
from a drinking spree to being sober, or back again.

4. The children are angry because they are repeatedly
disappointed, neglected, or abused by their parents when
they need their parents' protection most.

5. The children feel a sense of guilt and shame, in part because of the feelings they have toward their parents, in part because they may have assumed an unreasonable amount of responsibility for the parent's drinking.

Other authors have observed that certain characteristics of life in an alcoholic home predispose children to later problems. They include children assuming a parent's role, inconsistencies in relationships between children and their parents, poor examples parents in these homes set for their children, stress associated with being a member of these chaotic families, and inconsistent feelings children have toward their parents (sometimes love, other times hate or fear).

In *Taking Charge: How Families Can Climb Out of the Chaos of Addiction . . . and Flourish*, Doctors Schlesinger and Horberg describe the chaos of family life as filled with shame, hopelessness, panic, despair, and a feeling of vulnerability. Family members are caught in a cycle in which an ever-increasing amount of their energy is consumed by reacting to the drinker's actions, with little left over for creating a satisfying family life. Family members sometimes feel that their very survival, both psychological and physical, is at risk.

Taking Charge offers this description of the exasperation family members feel:

"*Life is chaotic.* You feel that your life—even your own behavior—is out of control. Promises you make to yourself are easily broken (e.g., 'no more concessions to my addicted wife,' 'I'll do my taxes,' 'I'll fix the furnace,' 'I'll take my child to the doctor'). There are phone calls in the middle of the night. The 'other shoe' drops and drops often. Consequences of self-neglect (things you've let go in the midst of a chaotic family life) terrorize you and your family.

"*You feel isolated.* Even in a crowd, you feel desperately lonely. You do not feel lovable or likable. When others respond to you with warmth, you wonder whether they would like you if they really knew you. You fear that they want something from you or that you have to cater to them, please them, or win their approval. So you *must* keep distant in order to survive as a person.

"*You are in a state of emotional pain.* Life traumatizes you so that you must either distract yourself or feel extreme levels of discomfort.

"*You are afraid to change.* Because you are convinced that life will work out badly for you, the prospect of change is very frightening.

"Typically, the individual feels that he:

a. does not know what would satisfy him,
b. could not get it if he knew what it was,
c. would not be entitled to it if he did manage to get it.
d. would lose it if he had it, and
e. would be rejected by others if he admitted that he enjoyed it.

"Pleasures are hidden, secret, taken on the sly. Sources of pleasure usually bring about pain, because the individual has not learned to gratify his deeper needs safely and responsibly. He suffers shame, rejection and loss because of the way he goes about meeting his needs.

"Typically, the individual is unable to:

a. pinpoint skills and strengths,
b. describe them accurately and consistently,
c. believe in his ability to succeed in challenging situations, and
d. commit himself to take on a challenge and follow through on the commitment.

"He often feels anxious, helpless, and inadequate; he feels panic and lacks confidence, despite his actual level of objective success. Victories are understood in grandiose terms that feel empty when examined. No practical understanding of his strengths is available to the individual in times of stress.

"Typically, the individual has trouble:

a. recognizing different feelings,
b. putting feelings into words,

    c. accepting his feelings ('I shouldn't feel this way'),
    d. telling other people about his feelings, and
    e. feeling secure after telling others about personal
       feelings.

"The individual is emotionally isolated. He feels overwhelmed and mystified by mood changes. Sometimes he feels a sense of panic; sometimes he feels numb. Mostly, he merely reacts to the chaos and confusion and feels helpless to stop it. A sense of shame develops, and he frequently gets depressed. When he experiences the trauma of a loss (loss of a hoped-for experience or loss of face), he may feel bad but often he loses awareness of the connection between the feelings and the events.

"In a state of exasperation, the individual often feels conscious of the need to escape."

These descriptions of family life depict an atmosphere that is likely to be hostile to healthy family life and individual growth. How might we expect children to turn out after being immersed in this type of environment in their formative years?

THE MAKEUP OF ACOAs

Several authors have suggested that children assume one of several roles in such family environments. In *Another Chance: Hope and Health for the Alcoholic Family*, Sharon Wegscheider described four possible roles. The *Hero* is the child who overachieves because of a sense of inadequacy and guilt. The *Scapegoat* acts out, sometimes in delinquent ways, because he feels hurt by the consequences of family life. The *Lost Child* chooses to be alone as his way of avoiding family chaos. The *Mascot* is the family clown who tries to relieve the family's tension by doing funny things.

Claudia Black, in her 1982 book *It Will Never Happen to Me*, describes the *Responsible One*, who resembles Wegscheider's Hero; the *Adjuster*, who, in a manner similar to the Lost Child, tries to banish from his mind both the chaos of family life and any feelings he has about it; the

Acting-Out Child, and the *Placater*, who is a great help to others in their emotional turmoil, but who characteristically stores his own emotions inside.

Adjusting to family chaos by assuming one of these roles can cause problems for a person if that role is carried forward unchanged into adult life. The most consistent characteristic that the authors we have mentioned (and others) describe is that of not expressing emotions effectively. This is likely a major contributing factor to the depression often seen by clinicians among ACOAs.

Adult Children of Alcoholics is the name of a national organization of self-help groups which was founded to meet the needs of ACOAs. Its literature includes a list of Attitudes and Character Traits that the organization believes are held by ACOAs. They capture the beliefs of a number of prominent writers in this area, including Janet Woititz and Dr. Robert Ackerman, and they form the basis of the approach the organization takes to the problems ACOAs experience.

Attitudes (Reactions to self-perceptions):
1. We judge ourselves harshly.
2. We take ourselves seriously and have difficulty having fun.
3. We are approval-seekers and fear personal criticism.
4. We feel isolated, different from other people.
5. We focus on others rather than look honestly at ourselves.
6. We are attracted to people who are rarely there emotionally for us.
7. We guess at what normal is.
8. We live from the viewpoint of victims.

Character Traits (Defenses developed as a result of having been raised in an alcoholic household):
1. We were overly responsible.
2. We were frightened by angry people and authority figures.

3. We need intimacy, yet have difficulty with intimate relationships.
4. We fear abandonment.
5. We have an exaggerated need to control.
6. We have strong guilt feelings.
7. We are overly reactive.
8. We are loyal to others even though that loyalty may be undeserved.
9. We stuff our feelings, unable to either feel or express them.
10. Our impulsivity leads to anger, self-hate, and loss of control.
11. We tend to look for immediate, rather than deferred gratification.
12. We are angry people.
13. We find it easier to give in to others than to stand up for ourselves.
14. We are addicted to excitement.
15. We often confuse love and pity.
16. We have a tendency toward procrastination.
17. We have difficulty trusting both ourselves and others.
18. We have problems with self-esteem.
19. We are anxious people, often dwelling on our past and future fears.
20. We have the potential for, and tendency towards, becoming alcoholics and/or marrying them.

Interestingly, a number of authors and researchers have considered the characteristics attributed to ACOAs and have concluded that they may apply equally well to adults who grew up in homes made chaotic by other means. In the Forward to *Adult Children of Alcoholics*, by far the best seller of books in this area, Janet Woititz acknowledges this when she writes, in part, that "we have learned that the material discussed applies to other dysfunctional families as well. . . . It appears that much of what is true for the children of alcoholics is also true for others, and that this understanding can help reduce the isolation of countless persons who also thought they were 'different' because of their life experience."

SOME PROMISING NEW RESEARCH

There is an important new trend to the findings from research in this area. Much of the research so far has centered on the harmful effects of growing up in alcoholic home. Indeed, the "wisdom" among therapists and others who have talked extensively to ACOAs who come for treatment or self-help group meetings is that these adult children have carried dysfunctional patterns of living and relationships with them from childhood, even if they seem to be well-adjusted adults. We do not want to minimize the harmful effects of growing up in an alcoholic home; for some ACOAs they can be devastating and of long duration. Indeed, some researchers suggest that growing up in chaotic families itself is a possible contributor to later problems, whether the chaos stems from a drinker or from some other source.

But it is important to note that recent research suggests that not all ACOAs face an inevitably bleak future. Some, it seems, can survive their early family life and do quite well later on.

We want to stress the promise this research gives us that a fuller understanding is possible of the complexities of growing up in an alcoholic family. At the same time, we are aware that any single study has its limitations and that the findings of one study are not conclusive. With that caution in mind, let us examine some of this research.

In a study of children of alcoholics, Dr. Emmy Warner found that not all children of alcoholics develop serious coping problems in childhood or adolescence. Her study focused on the differences between the children who did develop serious coping problems and those who functioned well, whom she described as "resilient" children of alcoholics.

The "resilient" children were found to have personal characteristics such as adequate intelligence, good communication skills, a desire for achievement and a belief that they were responsible for helping themselves with life problems. In addition, as infants, the "resilient" children got more attention and had parents who had good marriages. The important point of this study is that a parent's alcoholism does not, by itself, automatically produce problems for children later in their lives.

Support for this idea was found in a 1988 study by Doctors Berkowitz and Perkins. In comparing children of alcoholics with their college classmates, they found the ACOAs to be similar to their peers in many areas of personality functioning. The sex of the parent and the sex of the child made a difference in how severely the child was affected. For instance, daughters of alcoholic fathers seemed to experience the most damage to their self-esteem.

Certain other factors can also help immunize children from the negative forces of life in an alcoholic family. These factors take the form of strategies families and children adopt to deal with the chaos, unpredictability, and inconsistencies of the alcoholic family.

For example, in a recent study for her degree from the University of Maryland, Margaret Easley took a close took at the relationship between the way families handled the stress the alcoholism placed on the family and the development of later psychological problems and alcoholism. Hers was a search for possible factors that could immunize the child from the otherwise harmful effects of the chaotic life of an alcoholic family.

The Easley study suggested that several things might reduce the catastrophic impact of an alcoholic family atmosphere. First was the way in which family members looked at their problems. ACOAs from families that could see their problems as manageable were less likely to develop psychological problems later in life than were those who could not see past the overwhelming presence of the problems. The more families passively accepted their problems and could not develop hope that they could be overcome, the more likely their children would develop psychological problems and alcoholism later in life.

Problem-solving, which we mentioned in Chapter 3, seemed to play an important role in the later psychological health of ACOAs. Those from families that used problem-solving techniques to solve their problems were less likely to harbor feelings of anger and hostility later on.

Social support, which is emphasized in many approaches to recovery, seems vital. Families that developed effective outlets for support produced ACOAs who were less depressed than their isolated counterparts.

Family members who attempted to cope with the alcoholism in their midst by accepting responsibility for, or blaming themselves for, the drinking or who simply tried to escape from or avoid the chaos seemed to pay a higher price for their coping styles than those who tackled their problems more directly. The first group developed many more symptoms of physical and psychological disorders than the second.

The results of this study suggest that the impact of growing up in an alcoholic home are far more complex than originally thought and that not all children who grow up in these homes necessarily grow up with physical and psychological problems. In the words of Ms. Easley:

"Overall, the results of this study lend support to the idea that families and individuals who take control over their lives instead of seeing themselves as controlled by others are better able to maintain healthy functioning. . . . For those who do seek help, the importance of empowering the family members to take responsibility for their own lives, even if the drinking has not stopped, is strongly supported by this study. Additionally, it is essential that a clear distinction be made between accepting responsibility for the parent's alcoholism (which was related in the study to the development of psychological problems) and accepting responsibility for one's own life."

This clearly suggests that the lives of future ACOAs

need not necessarily be as uniformly bleak as we previously believed they would be.

RESOURCES

Among the resources available to ACOAs in many communities are self-help groups, therapy groups, and individual counseling or psychotherapy.

Self-Help Groups

In some cities, Al-Anon groups have either evolved into ACOA groups or helped establish ACOA groups organized around the Al-Anon principles. These groups offer all the advantages described in the chapter on Alcoholics Anonymous—no fees, no waiting lists, informal structure, good support, good availability. ACOAs often describe how helpful these groups can be, if only because of the opportunity they provide to discover that they are not alone in how they feel. In addition, some ACOAs first come to these meetings with very dim or even no memories of what occurred during portions of their childhood. (Pat Conroy aptly depicted this problem when a character in his book *Prince of Tides* was referred to as "the King of Unremembrance.") These people find both that their memories are jogged by listening to other group members and that more childhood feelings become accessible to them.

For further information about the national self-help group for children of alcoholics, contact:

National Association for Children of Alcoholics
31582 Coast Highway
Suite B
South Laguna, CA 92677
Phone: 714-499-3889

Therapy Groups

Therapy groups for ACOAs are usually available in outpatient alcoholism clinics or through private mental health practitioners. The nearest affiliate of the National

Council on Alcoholism usually can provide referrals to ACOA therapy groups. The groups offer some of the same advantages as self-help groups, such as support and resurrection of childhood memories. In addition, the group is usually led by a professional who can focus the group's energy and help the members learn about how they interact with others.

Individual Therapy

Some ACOAs do not feel ready to discuss their problems in a group setting and are best served by individual therapy at first. As with therapy groups, individual therapy for ACOAs is usually available in outpatient alcoholism clinics or through private mental health practitioners. It is important that the therapist have experience in the treatment of alcoholism and be conversant with the issues customarily encountered by ACOAs.

These three resources—self-help groups, therapy groups, and individual therapy—are not the only ones available to ACOAs. Family therapy, pastoral counseling, and college courses can all be helpful to ACOAs.

Reading pertinent literature can also be of great assistance. The National Association for Children of Alcoholics has a number of books and pamphlets that the organization recommends. Contact this group at the address and phone above. The following is a selected list of books on ACOAs if you would like to read further.

Taking Charge: How Families Can Climb out of the Chaos of Addiction . . . and Flourish by Stephen E. Schlesinger and Lawrence K. Horberg (New York: Fireside Books/ Simon and Schuster, 1988).

It Will Never Happen to Me! by Claudia Black (Denver: M.A.C. Publishing, 1981).

Adult Children of Alcoholics by Janet Woititz (Pompano Beach, FL: Health Communications, Inc., 1983).

Let Go and Grow by Robert J. Ackerman (Pompano Beach, FL: Health Communications, Inc., 1987).

Another Chance: Hope and Health for the Alcoholic Family by Sharon Wegscheider (Palo Alto, CA: Science and Behavior Books, Inc., 1981).

Children of Alcoholism: A Survivor's Manual by Judith Seixas and Geraldine Youcha (New York: Harper and Row, 1985).

Epilogue

The purpose of this book has not been to help you learn how drinkers might differ from other people. It has instead been to help you discover how drinkers are *like* others who have difficulty coping with their problems.

Your aim at this point, after having read through the book and done the exercises, is not necessarily to have found the answers that will ultimately make your life better. Instead, we hope that you have learned how to observe and analyze your actions and how to ask better questions about yourself. Ultimately, asking better questions will help you find more complete answers about your life.

The goal of making your life better is one that you might be able to achieve more readily if you allow others to help you. Even if you have learned to ask better questions about yourself, you might still need some direction and some assistance in changing your life. Some of that direction and assistance can come from this book. And for some people, that may be enough.

But our experience suggests that most people will find the task of changing their drinking habits—and, ultimately, changing their lives—quite formidable. For those who want it, help is available. In Appendix A is a listing of resources to which you can turn for information and assistance with the task that lies before you. Do not hesitate to call on the people and read the books and pamphlets we refer to in that listing.

We do not want to leave you with a bunch of dire warnings about your drinking problem and the attempts you might make to change it. On the other hand, we do not want to minimize the difficulty that similar attempts have presented among the people we have treated.

Perhaps the most prudent advice we can give you at this point is to turn for help if you think you will need it, and to go for that help before things get confusing and out of hand for you. We cannot recall many people who have come to us too *early*. Our files are full of those who would have done themselves a service by coming sooner.

Good luck!

PART 4
Resources

Appendix A

Resource Organizations

In this section, we have listed a number of sources of information to help you understand—and get help for—drinking problems. The listing here is certainly not exhaustive, but these resources will get you started on your search for information and help.

Governmental and Private Organizations

National Clearinghouse for Alcohol Information (NCALI)
Post Office Box 2345
Rockville, Maryland 20852
Phone: (301) 468-2600

NCAI is a branch of the United States Government Department of Health and Human Services (DHHS). It has a large and very useful collection of books, pamphlets, and references that it can either provide or direct you to. Write to NCALI for a listing of their publications and services.

National Council on Alcoholism, Inc.
12 West 21st Street
7th Floor
New York, New York 10010
Phone: (212) 206-6770

Write to NCA for information on alcoholism and its effects on health, family life and society.

Alcoholics Anonymous
Post Office Box 459
Grand Central Station
New York, New York 10017
     You can write to AA's national office for information
on Alcoholics Anonymous publications, on AA chapters
nationwide, and on Al-Anon, Alateen, and Alatot chapters
around the country. But before you do, check the white
pages of your local phone book under "Alcoholics Anonymous." You will probably find a local phone number to call,
and you will save yourself some time. Your local chapter
can refer you to local AA, Al-Anon, Alateen, and Alatot
resources.

Hazelden Educational Services
Box 176
Center City, Minnesota 55012
Phones: (800) 328-9288 (Continental United States)
          (612) 464-8844 or 464-3100 (Twin Cities Minne-
               sota area)
          (612) 257-4010 (Minnesota, outside of the Twin
               Cities area)
     Contact Hazelden for information on alcohol abuse and
other drug abuse publications. Hazelden's catalog contains
many of AA's publications, as well as a variety of other
publications and audiovisual aids dealing with addictive
problems.

National Association for Children of Alcoholics
31582 Coast Highway
Suite B
South Laguna, CA 92677
Phone: 714-499-3889
     Contact the National Association for information and
literature about adult children of alcoholics.

Finding an Alcoholism Treatment Center in Your Area

     There are several ways to start your search for an alco-
holism treatment center in your area. The first step is to

look for an agency, hospital, health or mental health center or private practitioner who can evaluate your need for treatment, including whether it would be better for you to enter a hospital or enroll in outpatient treatment.

But how do you do that? Consult your family physician, your clergyman, friends, relatives, neighbors, or anyone else you can think of who might know of treatment programs to which they can refer you. If you can, ask at your place of employment. (Remember, though, that some employers take an interest in their employees' drinking problems; others do not.) Look in your phone book yellow pages under "Alcoholism"; you will likely find listings of treatment programs. However, the yellow pages will mention only those programs that have paid for advertisements. There might be other programs in your area that do not advertise in the yellow pages. If you are a veteran of the U.S. armed services, you can contact the nearest Veterans Administration Hospital or clinic.

You can also contact the office of your state government which specializes in alcoholism services. Appendix D is a listing of those offices for each of the 50 states and for U.S. territories.

If none of these alternatives works for you, you might turn to a federal publication which lists treatment organizations nationwide.

Resources for Drunk Driving

There are some things you can do about drunk driving beyond taking care to monitor your own driving condition carefully. Your governor's office may have a Highway Safety Representative who can tell you about efforts in your state to combat drunk driving problems. Contact the office for your state listed in Appendix E. In addition, the U.S. Department of Transportation can provide a list of resources on efforts to address the drunk driving problem nationwide. Write to the National Highway Traffic Safety Administration, Washington, DC 20590 for more information.

An interesting project has recently been initiated to help parents and children deal with the problem of teenage drunk driving. An organization called Students Against Driving Drunk (SADD) has formulated a Contract for Life to be discussed and signed by parent and child. The Contract is an agreement that each will refrain from driving when impaired by alcohol. Parents agree, in addition, to pick up or to provide other transportation for their teenagers who call when they are intoxicated and cannot drive. A copy of the Contract for Life can be obtained by writing to SADD, 110 Pleasant Street, Corbin Plaza, Marlboro, Massachusetts 01752.

The Contract for Life provides a handy way to talk to your teenage driver about the problem of drunk teenage driving. SADD will also help you start a local SADD chapter in your area, if one does not already exist. Write them for details if you are interested.

Appendix B

Analyzing Drinking Patterns

Step 1: Things that preceded your drinking. Our first step in this venture is for you to think of times when you were drinking. Ask yourself what was happening immediately before you wanted (or needed) a drink. What was going on? Where were you and with whom? List as many situations as you can.

Step 2: Emotions associated with Step 1. Now ask yourself, "What was I feeling? What were my emotions at the time?" Start by completing this sentence: I felt_____. Be careful; in this day and age we often use "I feel" when we mean "I think." In other words, we often think we're talking about thoughts. Here you want *emotions*. Here's a simple test: If you can substitute "I think" for "I feel" in your sentence, and if the sentence still makes sense, then you've got a thought and not an emotion. Try again. When you've listed a number of different situations with their associated emotions, combine them into groups according to the emotions that they have in common as in the last illustration. Now go to Step 3.

Step 3: Warning signs. Step 3 stems from a very simple principle: If you are going to head off the solution—drinking—that you have learned for coping with each emotion, you must first learn to recognize the emotional reaction itself. So, for each group you have identified in Step 2, try now to figure out how you know when you are experiencing that emotion. For instance, if one emotion you have identified is nervousness, how do you know you're nervous? How do you feel it? Do you tremble? Does your stomach churn? Do you have muscle cramps? What is it like for you? If another emotion is frustration, repeat the process, and so on. Call these things you are identifying the "warning signs" which tell you early on that you are experiencing these emotions.

Step 4: How alcohol helped. Think about what alcohol did to help you cope with the emotional reaction you identified in Step 2. If you were nervous, for example, did alcohol help you calm down? Did it do something else for you? List all the things it did to help you cope with each emotional reaction you identified.

Step 5: Other things that could help. Now think about what else you could do in order to accomplish what the alcohol did for you. If, for instance, alcohol helped you calm down when you were nervous, try to identify other things that might be able to do what the alcohol did.

Appendix C

Worksheet

Instructions: First, take a piece of paper and list what you gave up as a result of your drinking. List all the negative consequences of your drinking. (You know them only too well.) Now set that piece of paper aside. Concentrate on the five steps in the outline.

Step 1 Things that preceded my drinking	Step 2 Emotions associated with Step 1	Step 3 Warning signs	Step 4 What alcohol did for me/what I got from drinking	Step 5 What else could do what alcohol did?

Step 1 Things that preceded my drinking	Step 2 Emotions associated with Step 1	Step 3 Warning signs	Step 4 What alcohol did for me/what I got from drinking	Step 5 What else could do what alcohol did?

Appendix D

State and Regional Alcoholism Programs

This directory of state alcoholism programs is based on one compiled by the National Clearinghouse for Alcohol Information. Because addresses and telephone numbers may change, you might want to contact:

National Clearinghouse for Alcohol and Drug Information
PO Box 2345
Rockville, MD 20852
301-468-2600

Alabama

Alcoholism Program
Department of Mental
   Health
200 Interstate Pk Dr-Box
   3710
Montgomery, AL 36193
205-271-9253

Alaska

Office of Alcoholism and
   Drug Abuse

Pouch H-05F
Juneau, AK 99811
907-586-6201

Arizona

Alcohol Abuse Section
   Division of Behavioral
   Health Svcs
2500 E Van Buren St
Phoenix, AZ 85008
602-255-1238

Arkansas

Office of Alcohol and Drug
  Abuse Prevention
1515 West 7th Ave Ste 310
Little Rock, AR 72201
501-371-2603

California

Department of Alcohol and
  Drug Programs
111 Capitol Mall
Sacramento, CA 95814
916-445-1940

Colorado

Colorado Department of
  Health
Alcohol & Drug Abuse
  Division
4210 East 11th Ave
Denver, CO 80220
303-320-6137

Connecticut

Connecticut Alcohol and
  Drug Abuse Commission
999 Asylum Ave 3rd Fl
Hartford, CT 06105
203-566-2089

Delaware

Alcoholism Services
Lower Kensington
Environmental Ctr
1910 N Dupont Highway
New Castle, DE 19720
302-421-6111

District of Columbia

Alcoholism and Drug Abuse
  Administration, Central
  Office
1875 Connecticut Ave
  Ste 837
Washington, DC 20009

Florida

Alcohol & Drug Abuse
  Program
Department of Health &
  Rehab
1317 Winewood Blvd
Tallahassee, FL 32301
904-488-0900

Georgia

Alcohol and Drug Abuse
  Service Station
878 Peachtree St Ste 319
Atlanta, GA 30309
404-894-4785

Hawaii

Alcohol and Drug Abuse
  Branch
PO Box 3378
Honolulu, HI 96801
808-548-4280

Idaho

Substance Abuse Section
Health & Welfare
  Department
450 W State St
Boise, ID 83720
208-334-4368

Illinois

Department of Mental
  Health & Developmental
  Disabilities
902 S Wind Rd
Springfield, IL 62703
217-786-6314

Indiana

Division of Addiction
  Services
429 N Pennsylvania St
Indianapolis, IN 46204
317-232-7816

Iowa

Iowa Dept of Substance
  Abuse
507 10th St Ste 500
Des Moines, IA 50319
515-281-3641

Kansas

Kansas Alcohol & Drug
  Abuse Svcs, Dept of Social
  & Rehab
Biddle Bldg-2700 W 6th St
Topeka, KS 66606
913-296-3925

Kentucky

Division of Substance Abuse
Dept for MHMR Services
275 E Main St
Frankfort, KY 40621
502-564-2880

Louisiana

Office of Prevention &
  Recovery from Alcohol &
  Drug Abuse
2744B Wooddale Blvd
Baton Rouge, LA 70805
504-922-0728

Maine

Office of Alcoholism and
  Drug Abuse Prevention
State House Stn 11
Augusta, ME 04333
207-289-2781

Maryland

Alcoholism Control
  Administration
201 SW Preston St 4th Fl
Baltimore, MD 21202
301-383-2781

Massachusetts

Division of Alcoholism
150 Tremont St
Boston, MA 02111
617-727-1960

Michigan

Office of Substance Abuse
  Svcs
Dept of Public Health
3500 N Logan
Lansing, MI 48914
517-373-8600

Minnesota

Chemical Dependency Prog
Div
Dept of Human Services
444 Lafayette Rd
St Paul, MN 55101
612-296-3991

Mississippi

Division of Alcohol & Drug
Abuse
1102 Robert E Lee Bldg
Jackson, MS 39201
601-359-1297

Missouri

Division of Alcohol & Drug
Abuse
Dept of Mental Health
2002 Missouri Blvd
Jefferson City, MO 65101
314-751-4942

Montana

Department of Institutions
Alcohol & Drug Abuse
Division
1539 11th Ave
Helena, MT 59620
406-444-2827

Nebraska

Division of Alcoholism and
Drug Abuse
Box 94728
Lincoln, NE 68509
402-471-2851

Nevada

Bureau of Alcohol & Drug
Abuse
505 King St Kinkead Bldg
500
Carson City, NV 89701
702-885-4790

New Hampshire

New Hampshire Office of
A & D Abuse Prevention
H & W Bldg Hazen Dr
Concord, NH 03301
603-271-4627

New Jersey

Division of Alcoholism
CN 362
Trenton, NJ 08625
609-292-8947

New Mexico

Alcoholism Bureau
Behavioral Health
Services Division
PO Box 968
Santa Fe, NM 87504
505-984-0020

New York

NYS Division of Alcoholism
& Alcohol Abuse
194 Washington Ave
Albany, NY 12210
518-474-3377

North Carolina

Alcohol and Drug Abuse
  Svcs
Division of Human
  Resources
325 N Salisbury St
Raleigh, NC 27611
919-829-4670

North Dakota

Division of Alcoholism &
  Drug Abuse, Dept of
  Human Services
Judicial Wing 3rd Fl
  Capitol
Bismarck, ND 58505
701-224-2769

Ohio

Bureau on Alcohol Abuse
  and Alcoholism Recovery
170 N High St 3rd Fl
Columbus, OH 43215
614-466-3445

Oklahoma

Department of Mental
  Health
Programs Division
PO Box 53277 Capitol
  Station
Oklahoma City, OK 73105
405-521-0044

Oregon

Programs for Alcohol and
  Drug Problems

301 Public Service Bldg
Salem, OR 97310
503-378-2163

Pennsylvania

PA Dept of Health
Office of D&A Programs
PO Box 90
Harrisburg, PA 17108
717-787-9857

Rhode Island

Division of Substance Abuse
Detoxification Unit
412 Howard Ave Ben Rush
  Bldg
Cranston, RI 02920
401-464-2531

South Carolina

South Carolina
Commission on Alcohol
  and Drug Abuse
3700 Forest Dr Ste 300
Columbia, SC 29204
803-758-2521

South Dakota

State Department of Health
Div of Alcohol & Drug
  Abuse
Joe Foss Bldg 523 E Capitol
Pierre, SD 57501-3182
605-773-3123

Tennessee

Tennessee Dept of Mental
Hlth
Div of A&D Abuse Svcs
505 Deaderick St 4th Fl
Nashville, TN 37219
615-741-1921

Texas

Commission on Alcoholism
1705 Guadalupe
Austin, TX 78701
512-475-2577

Utah

Division of Alcoholism &
Drugs
PO Box 45500
150 SW N Temple 350
Salt Lake City,
UT 84145-0500
801-533-6532

Vermont

Office of Alcohol and Drug
Abuse Programs
103 S Main St
Waterbury, VT 05676
802-241-2170

Virginia

Office of Substance Abuse
Department of Mental
Health
PO Box 1797
Richmond, VA 23214
804-768-1524

Washington

Office on Alcoholism, Dept
of Social and Health
Services
Mail Stop OB-44W
Olympia, WA 98504
206-753-5866

West Virginia

Div on Alcoholism & Drug
Abuse
West Virginia Dept of
Health
1800 Washington St E
Charleston, WV 25305
304-348-2276

Wisconsin

Office of Alcohol & Other
Drug Abuse
1 W Wilson St-PO Box 7851
Madison, WI 53707
608-266-2717

Wyoming

Substance Abuse Division of
Community Programs
State Office Bldg
Cheyenne, WY 82002
307-777-7115

Appendix E

State Highway Safety Offices

Alabama

Director
Office of Highway and
  Traffic Safety
State Highway Building,
  Room 741
11 South Union St
Montgomery, AL 36130
  Phone: (205) 832-5974

Alaska

Commissioner
Department of Public Safety
Pouch N
Juneau, AK 99801
  Phone: (907) 465-4300

Arizona

Governor's Highway Safety
  Representative
Department of
  Transportation

206 S. 17th St
Phoenix, AZ 85007
  Phone: (602) 261-7559

Arkansas

Director
Arkansas Highway Safety
  Program
#1 Capitol Mall
Level 4B, Suite 215
Little Rock, AR 72201
  Phone: (501) 371-1101

California

Director
Office of Traffic Safety
Business and
  Transportation Agency
7000 Franklin Blvd,
  Suite 330
Sacramento, CA 95823
  Phone: (916) 445-5373

Colorado

Director
Division of Highway Safety
4201 East Arkansas Ave
Denver, CO 80222
    Phone: (303) 757-9381

Connecticut

Governor's Representative
Department of
    Transportation
Bureau of Highways
24 Wolcott Hill Rd
Wethersfield, CT 06109
    Phone: (203) 566-4248

Delaware

Governor's Representative
    for Highway Safety
Treadway Towers
9 East Loockerman St
Dover, DE 19901
    Phone: (302) 736-4282

District of Columbia

Director
D.C. Department of
    Transportation
Presidential Building,
    Room 508
415 12th St, N.W.
Washington, DC 20004
    Phone: (202) 727-5847

Florida

Director
Division of Public Safety
    Planning and Assistance

Florida Department of
    Veteran and Community
    Affairs
    Phone: (904) 488-6001

Georgia

Director
Office of Highway Safety
    State of Georgia
2175 Northlake Parkway
Building 4, Suite 144
Tucker, GA 30084
    Phone: (404) 393-7480

Hawaii

Governor's Highway Safety
    Representative
Department of
    Transportation
869 Punchbowl St
Honolulu, HI 96813
    Phone: (808) 548-4655

Idaho

Director
Idaho Department of
    Transportation
Box 7129
Boise, ID 83707
    Phone: (208) 384-3699

Illinois

Director
Division of Traffic Safety
319 Administration Bldg
2300 South Dirksen Pkwy
Springfield, IL 62764
    Phone: (217) 782-4972

Indiana

Executive Assistant
Governor's Representative
State Capitol-Room 210
Indianapolis, Indiana 46204
   Phone: (317) 232-4579

Iowa

Director
Office for Planning and
   Programming
Capitol Hill Annex
523 East 12th St
Des Moines, IA 50319
   Phone: (515) 281-6483

Kansas

Secretary
Kansas Department of
   Transportation
State Office Building
Topeka, KS 66612
   Phone: (913) 296-3461

Kentucky

Commissioner
Bureau of State Police
Department of Justice
State Office Building
Frankfort, KY 40601
   Phone: (502) 564-4890

Louisiana

Executive Director
Louisiana Highway Safety
   Commission
P.O. Box 66336
Baton Rouge, LA 70896
   Phone: (504) 925-6991

Maine

Official Highway Safety
   Representative
Department of Public Safety
36 Hospital St
Augusta, ME 04330
   Phone: (207) 289-2551

Maryland

Secretary of Transportation
P.O. Box 8755
Baltimore-Washington
   International Airport
Baltimore, MD 21240
   Phone: (301) 859-7397

Massachusetts

Director
Governor's Highway Safety
   Bureau
100 Charles River Plaza,
   9th Floor
Boston, MA 02114
   Phone: (617) 727-5074

Michigan

Executive Director
Office of Highway Safety
   Planning
111 S. Capitol Ave,
   Lower Level
Lansing, MI 48913
   Phone: (517) 373-8011

Minnesota

Commissioner
Department of Public Safety
 Transportation Building
St. Paul, MN 55155
 Phone: (612) 296-6642

Mississippi

Governor's Representative
 for Highway Safety
Governor's Highway Safety
 Program
510 George St, Suite 246
Jackson, MS 39201
 Phone: (601) 354-6892

Missouri

Director
Department of Public Safety
P.O. Box 749
Jefferson City, MO 65101
 Phone: (314) 751-4905

Montana

Administrator
Highway Traffic Safety Div
Department of Justice
303 North Roberts
Helena, MT 59620
 Phone: (406) 449-3412

Nebraska

Director
Department of Motor
 Vehicles
State Office Building
State House Station 94789

Lincoln, NE 68509
 Phone: (402) 471-2281

Nevada

Governor's Highway Safety
 Representative
Director
555 Wright Way, Rm. 258
Carson City, NV 89711
 Phone: (702) 885-5375
 Phone: (603) 271-2131

New Hampshire

Coordinator
New Hampshire Highway
 Safety Agency
Pine Inn Plaza
117 Manchester St
Concord, NH 03301

New Jersey

Director
Division of Motor Vehicles
State of New Jersey
25 South Montgomery St
Trenton, NJ 08666
 Phone: (609) 292-4570

New Mexico

Secretary of Transportation
 Department
P.E.R.A. Building,
 Room 220
P.O. Box 1028
Santa Fe, NM 87503
 Phone: (505) 827-2045

New York

Commissioner
New York Department of
    Motor Vehicles
The Governor Nelson A.
    Rockefeller Empire State
    Plaza
Albany, NY 12228
    Phone: (518) 474-0841

North Carolina

Director
Governor's Highway Safety
    Program
215 East Lane St
Raleigh, NC 27601
    Phone: (919) 733-3083

North Dakota

Highway Commissioner
North Dakota Highway
    Department
600 East Boulevard Ave
Bismarck, ND 58505-0178
    Phone: (701) 224-2581

Ohio

Director
Department of Highway
    Safety
P.O. Box 7167
Columbus, OH 43205
    Phone: (614) 466-2550

Oklahoma

Governor's Representative
Oklahoma Highway Safety
    Office

Oklahoma Department of
    Transportation Building
200 N.E. 21st Street, D-4
Oklahoma City, OK 73105
    Phone: (405) 521-3314

Oregon

Governor's Representative
Oregon Traffic Safety
    Commission
State Library Building,
    4th Floor
Salem, OR 97310
    Phone: (503) 378-3670

Pennsylvania

Deputy Secretary for Safety
    Administration
Commonwealth of
    Pennsylvania
1200 Transportation and
    Safety Building
Harrisburg, PA 17120
    Phone: (717) 787-3928

Rhode Island

Director
Department of
    Transportation
Governor's Highway Safety
    Representative
State Office Building
Smith St
Providence, RI 02903
    Phone: (401) 277-2481

South Carolina

Director
Division of Public Safety
   Programs
Edgar A. Brown State
   Office Building
1205 Pendleton St,
   Room 401
Columbia, SC 29201
   Phone: (803) 758-3573

South Dakota

Director
Division of Highway Safety
Department of Public Safety
118 West Capitol Ave
Pierre, SD 57501
   Phone: (605) 773-4124

Tennessee

Commissioner
Department of
   Transportation
James K. Polk State Office
   Building
505 Deaderick St
Suite 700
Nashville, TN 37219
   Phone: (615) 741-2848

Texas

Governor's Representative
State Department of
   Highways and Public
   Transportation
11th and Brazos

Austin, TX 78701
   Phone: (512) 475-3525

Utah

Commissioner
Department of Public Safety
4501 South 2700 West
Salt Lake City, UT 84119
   Phone: (801) 965-4461

Vermont

Secretary of Transportation
133 State St
Montpelier, VT 05602
   Phone: (802) 828-2657

Virginia

Director
Department of
   Transportation Safety
P.O. Box 27412
Richmond, VA 23269
   Phone: (804) 276-9600,
   Ext. 20

Washington

Director
Washington Traffic Safety
   Commission
1000 Cherry St
Olympia, WA 98504
   Phone: (206) 753-6197

West Virginia

Governor's Highway Safety
   Representative

Governor's Office of
  Economic and
  Community Development
5790-A MacCorkle Ave
Charleston, WV 25304
  Phone: (304) 348-8814

Wisconsin

Secretary, Wisconsin Office
  of Highway Safety
P.O. Box 7910
4802 Sheboygan Ave
Madison, WI 53707
  Phone: (608) 266-1113

Wyoming

State Highway Safety
  Engineer
Wyoming Highway Safety
  Department
Highway Safety Branch
P.O. Box 1708
Cheyenne, WY 82001
  Phone: (307) 777-7296

American Samoa

Governor's Representative
Executive Office Building
Government of American
  Samoa
Pago Pago, American
  Samoa 96799
  Phone: (639-9188 or 82)
  (Through International
  Operator)

Guam

Governor's Highway Safety
  Representative
Department of Public
  Works
P.O. Box 2950
Agana, Guam 96910
  Phone: 646-5831, Ext. 11
  (Through International
  Operator)

Virgin Islands

Governor's Representative
Virgin Island Office of
  Highway Safety
P.O. Box 1847
Fredericksted, St. Croix
Virgin Islands 00840
  Phone: (809) 772-3025

Northern Mariana Islands

Director of Public Safety
Office of Highway Safety
Department of Public Safety
Commonwealth of the
  Northern Mariana
  Islands
Saipan, Northern Mariana
  Islands 96950
  Phone: 6333/6431
  (Through International
  Operator)

Puerto Rico

Secretary of Transportation
  and Public Works

Minillas Government
  Center
12th Floor
Santurce, Puerto Rico 00910
  Phone: (809) 726-5290
           (809) 726-5150,
           Ext. 3550

Indian Tribes

Commissioner of Indian
  Affairs
Bureau of Indian Affairs
Department of the Interior
19th & C Streets, N.W.
Washington, D.C. 20242
  Phone: (505) 766-2863

Index